Adrian Mitchell is one of Britain's most popular poets, his works including *Ride the Nightmare*, *Out Loud* and *The Apeman Cometh*. His literary expertise is borne out by many operas, films, television shows and plays that he has written and edited. His novels include *If you see me comin'* and *The Bodyguard* and his play *Tyger* was successfully staged at the National Theatre.

Man Friday, Adrian Mitchell's latest novel, was first seen as a TV play, followed closely by the film of the same name, *Man Friday*.

Adrian Mitchell

Man Friday

Futura Publications Limited

A Futura Book

01076501

First published in 1975
by Futura Publications Limited

Copyright © Adrian Mitchell 1975

Printed in Great Britain by
Hazell Watson & Viney Ltd
Aylesbury, Bucks
ISBN 0 8600 7274 6

67787422

Futura Publications Limited
Warner Road, London SE5

CONTENTS

5

6

CHAPTER ONE

In Which Music is Played and the Tribe Gathers to Listen to a Story

Somewhere, a long way from the trade routes, far in the warm indigo breadth of the ocean, a small island was awake in the early night and thumping out its strongest music.

The island had no name in any white language. But its own dark brown people called it by a thousand different names. It was important to keep inventing new names for the island. The tribe believed that the island enjoyed such attention.

The tribe. They were a lucky and gentle collection of characters, varying between five hundred and a thousand in numbers over the years. There are primitive tribes which are cruel, there are primitive tribes which are competitive. There are reasons and excuses for such tribes. But this tribe was not interested in either hurting or competing. It was an exceptionally happy and co-operative tribe.

Finding itself on an island overgrown with fruit and vegetables, overcrowded with pigs and goats and entirely surrounded by fish, there was more than enough for everyone to eat. Crops grew well from the dark earth and there was always plenty of time. Time for dancing, time for singing.

No-one was too stiff to dance. No-one was too tight around the throat to sing. And on this particular night, the night we are watching now, a story would be sung which was of importance to every member of the tribe.

They emerged from their huts. Each hut displayed the personality of its inhabitants by its shape, carvings, paintings on its walls, beads and feathers hung about the doorposts. The huts of the people were arranged in rough circles around an enormous meeting hut. Around the entire settlement there was no wall.

Tall fires jumped in the compound of flat, tight, bare earth in front of the meeting hut. The tribe danced facing the fires, knees bent, smiles widening – always facing the light of the fires. For, just as a baby always reaches towards the light, the tribe enjoyed light wherever they found it. That was their way.

Drums of all kinds wove a web of rhythm. Drums popping, exploding, working, scratching, weaving and thudding. Different rhythms exchanging opinions. The tribe chanted alongside and over the drums and the sound of the slapping and thudding of their own feet, chanting as they chose, as they changed, chanting whatever floated into their minds.

Every dance has a meaning. There are war dances, peace dances, love dances, sickness dances, curse dances, blessing dances, drought dances and a thousand more. This dance was a dance of preparation, a dance of getting ready to listen to a story. Such a dance should comfort each part of your body and clear all the clouds from your head so that you are able to see every image which the story-teller offers to you.

A dancing tribe – children, adults, old people swaying and mostly smiling. No two bodies dancing the same way, but all dancing together.

Three girls with bamboo flutes, shrilling above the drums, dancing around a boy and trying to drive him into higher and higher leaps from the ground up to the stars.

Seven small boys and girls taking it in turns to dance with a pet goat. The goat as tame and fond as an old dog, his golden eyes huge in the firelight.

A group of old men and women with their arms round each others' shoulders moving in a slow circular tortoise dance.

Two lovers teasing each other by moving their bodies so close that they almost slotted together as they stood and shook.

A relaxed and lanky man dancing alone with precise, high kicks into the air, laughing to himself.

A girl and a boy of about fifteen years old moving towards the meeting hut, carrying between them a gourd painted to resemble a toucan bird. The gourd was heavy and full of palm-wine. The dancers watched as the gourd moved between their galaxies. Their dances began to taper away and they began to follow the boy and girl, entering the great hut, passing under the ancient painted carving of the great bird with its wings outstretched and ready to fly forever.

In the centre of the great hut the boy and the girl set down the gourd carefully. They bowed to it. Then they both smiled and bowed to each other. Men, women and children, expectant and quietly excited, took their seats on the ground. Bowls were filled and passed around.

Among them, staring quietly at the earth, sat the man who was to tell the story. Among the tribe he had many names, but we will call him by his English name – 'Friday'. He had been away, he had been away from his people for many years. He had only returned to his own home island two days and two nights ago. He was full of longing to tell his story and the tribe longed to hear it, he was full of longing, but full of dread as well. Not that he felt any dread for his own people, he did not fear them at all. All that he was afraid of was that he might not tell his story well enough. His body was trembling, but he had expected that. A calm man cannot tell a story.

An old woman stretched her arm out, palm upwards, towards 'Friday'. All the members of the tribe looked towards him. They stretched out their hands to him in the same way. He placed his face in his hands, gently, staring into the darkness of his own eyelids. Then he looked up. The hands were all outstretched to him, inviting him to begin. The tribe's doctor spoke the usual words:

'Whether it hurts you or whether it pleases you; whether it

hurts us or whether it pleases us – it is time for you to tell the story.'

'Friday' slowed down his breathing. He must make sure his breath would serve him well. For tonight he had to tell a true story on which the future might be decided.

'It is time,' he said.

He stood. An old friend passed him a long, single-stringed instrument. He twanged it a few times out of rhythm, finding the feeling of it, finding the feeling of himself and his story, preparing to sing and dance his way through the night. Then he struck a rhythm from the string which the tribe's best musicians picked up and clarified. Once the first rhythm was established he was ready to twist and turn his way into his improvised recitation. 'Friday' began to sing:

> 'As we have always been together,
> Let us drink together.
> As we are together now,
> Let us dream together.
> Let the wine flow,
> Let my words flow
> And I will try to tell my story truly,
> As truly as I worship you,
> My own people.'

He stamped his foot three times and the drums doubled their pace. A flute began to fly.

> 'I am going to tell you about
> A red-faced monster with a man inside its belly.'

Some of the small children gasped. The older children hugged their knees and grinned.

> 'I am going to tell you about
> A gabbling goat who could spit deadly thunder.'

Incredulous looks from the middle-aged. Looks which said: nothing is impossible, from the old.

> 'I am going to tell you about
> The man whose spirit walks in darkness,
> The man who walks outside. . . .'

They had seen the strange man, the crimson man, the goat-hair man. 'Friday' moved his hands slowly apart from each other, palms downwards. The rhythm responded by slowing and subsiding.

> 'Close your eyes and see the story.
> Close your eyes and see the story.
> Close your eyes and see the story.'

This was the triple chant which signalled the real beginning. The people of the tribe closed their eyes when they were ready. 'Friday' made sure that all their eyes were closed. Then he laid down his one-string instrument, closed his eyes, and began to tell the story.

CHAPTER TWO

In Which I am Cast Away on a Desert Island, Lose Four Friends and Meet a Strange Creature

You know my stories. This will be my strangest story. Believe as much of it as you can. I will not tell you any lies on purpose. The story matters. The story matters to the tribe.

Several years ago, when you last saw me, and my face was clearer than it is today, five of us went fishing in the long canoe, the one with a toucan carved at its bow. Five of us, cheerful and clever fishermen. Encouraged by the eagerness of the fish to be caught and the kindness of the afternoon sun, we did not notice that currents were carrying us too far from this island. We did not see the sky's war-clouds assembling on the horizon.

With the sunset a storm broke, a massive night storm which doubled, tripled and quadrupled the height of waves. The storm picked us up in its right hand and hurled us across the ocean. It broke the back of our canoe. It swallowed all five of us down. And then it sicked us up on a beach we had never seen before, a fine-sanded beach.

I awoke there in the morning to find myself lying on my stomach. The island looked unused. Its shape appeared long and narrow, like a tall man outstretched in sleep. It rose to rocky heights, the slopes of the hills thick with green. The trees were shaking with birds. My body and mind were heavy. Then I looked down and saw my four friends lying on the beach.

One of them was dead. You remember old Hookloser, who used to tell the funniest stories of them all, Hookloser who was once chased for a mile by a mother eagle, Hookloser who was once so pleased with the look of his hut when he had painted it that he painted himself? Well, he was so full of water that we couldn't bring him back to life. We tried the usual spells, massage and dances, but nothing worked.

We made a journey bird for him. We laid many thin sticks in the shape of a good bird. We filled the spaces between the sticks with flowers which were his favourites. Then we curled old Hookloser into the belly of the bird as if he were an egg. We arranged dry wood around his body, close to him on every side, so that we could cook and eat him. For we all wanted to take some of the spirit of that man, whom we loved, into the dangerous future with us.

We cooked him with care and then began to eat moderately, each one taking his turn to tell some funny or sad story about old Hookloser. And there were many stories in his life, most of them glad stories. But we had not finished the ceremony when death visited us again.

From out of the undergrowth stepped an amazing creature. It was very tall and huge and it moved, roaring, towards us. Wild long white and brown hair bulged and sprouted all over its body. Its face was a sunset crimson. It was, you could tell when you looked at it very closely, a human creature of some sort in the clothing of a giant goat god. But the strangest thing of all was that its eyes were blue. From its shoulder protruded a long, shining stick which had the appearance of some magical instrument. This stick, I learned much later, is called a musket or gun.

My friend Ivory walked towards the goat-god, smiling. One of Ivory's hands was extended in greeting. I could tell he wanted to touch the shining musket. The shining of it was attractive. But the goat-god pulled his musket closer to his shoulder. Suddenly Ivory jerked into the air in pain, then he had collapsed on the sand and blood was spouting from his stomach, and Ivory was screaming, and there had been a great bang and smoke hung in the air and stank.

Poor Ivory, who used to sing so loudly, and badly, and happily. The other two ran. But I did not run. I did not run away from death, knowing that the faster you run away from him, the sooner he overtakes you. Oh, it was very bad.

First, the goat-god put down his musket. Then he raised two smaller shining sticks, called pistols. Weaver, the most cunning craftsman in all our tribe, was hit in the middle of his long back by the fire from one of these pistols. And Weaver crashed upon the sand and let his blood run fast.

Then Bentnose, who painted the poles of this meeting hut, ran as fast as he could into the sea, beating at the waves with his hands, trying to find a refuge in the water. But the second pistol killed him in the head.

I put vines around my wrists, as we do when we wish to show that we are not killers and have no desire to be killed. I crouched upon the sand and waited.

The goat-god walked towards me slowly. Then he placed his foot for a moment upon my neck. I did not speak. Then he said:

'What's this? A prisoner? You poor savage?'

He pulled the vines away from my wrists and stood back. He looked at me as if he feared I might suddenly change my form and become a snake. I opened my hands to say peace. He moved another step away.

'I have come to rescue you from the clutches of these foul cannibals,' he said, then motioned me to stand. I thought at that moment that he was going to kill me too with one of his sticks, but I stood up anyway.

It is very strange to see blue eyes for the first time. But once you can overcome the oddness of the colour, there is a freshness in them. I thought, at that time, that I could see some hope behind those eyes.

'Follow me,' he said. 'I have saved your life. And, what is more, I shall attempt to save your benighted soul.'

At the time, of course, I understood none of his words. But later, when I had learned to speak his tongue, he repeated to me, roughly, what he remembered having said at our early meetings.

I was staring at the beach. Three of my friends lay there in their own blood. I could see the terrible red holes in their flesh where their deaths had walked in. The goat-god pushed me towards the body of Bentnose. He put one hand on my shoulder, raised a finger, then picked up a large piece of driftwood.

'Dig big holes,' he shouted. 'Dig!'

The goat-god began to shovel up quantities of dry sand in a frenzied manner. Then he handed the driftwood to me and said: 'Now you do. Dig.'

I understood what he wanted, a hole in the sand, so I dug a great hole, only stopping when he held my driftwood back. Then he began to roll the body of Bentnose towards the hole. He had this horrible idea that dead people should be hidden away in holes below the sand. I am sorry. I should have liked to have eaten my friends to honour them, rather than leave them to be feasted on by the deep sand-creatures, but I was not allowed to do so. I had to lay them, one by one, in great, square holes in the sand. And then he made me cover their bodies over with sand.

As I worked, he read to me in a deep voice from a large black object called a book. A book is a collection of very tiny painted marks. Each mark has a meaning. They are painted by wise men in order to tell the people what to do. Don't laugh, there are many tribes in the world in which the people are told what to do by their elders or their leaders or sometimes, through books, by wise men who are dead. Of course it is a joke to us to take advice from a dead man ...

He read to me these words: 'In the sweat of thy face shall

thou eat bread, till thou return unto the ground; for out of it thou was taken. For dust thou art, and unto dust shall thou return.'

But then he stopped reading and began shouting. Apparently he could not find me. Thinking that he meant to shoot me, I had dug a hole for myself and was lying, curled up and waiting for the shot, at the bottom of the hole. He reached down and grabbed me by the arm. He pulled me out.

'No, no!' he shouted. 'Only when you die. Now we go home. I will show you where I live.'

He pushed me towards a path which led away from the beach. I obeyed. He walked behind me, prodding me every now and then with his musket-stick. You have all been followed by a nightmare at some time, I think? Then you know how I was feeling then, followed by that creature of such killing magic.

CHAPTER THREE

In Which I am Shown My New Home and See Many Wonders Before I Sleep

I followed behind the goat-god's huge, furred shoes as he climbed a hard mud path up a steep hill of palms. The marks of his shoes were everywhere about us. The palm trees at least were familiar, they were no different from the palm trees on our island, so I shall not bother to describe them. The path began to level out at a point high above the sea. We stopped. Before us stood a high wall of sharpened wooden stakes, too high and smooth for a man to climb. As I looked at that wall I wondered how many people were in the tribe of the goat-god, waiting behind that wall to do their worst to me.

He took hold of a piece of the wooden wall in one hand and pulled it towards him. A rope was attached to it, and when the rope was pulled it pulled something else. Suddenly there was a flying noise and a wooden ladder swung over the top of the stockade, and almost hit me on the head. I shouted with fright, but he laughed, clapped me on the shoulder and pointed to the ladder. It seemed he was very proud of this invention. Then he pushed me towards it. I was trying to work out why he had laughed when I was nearly hit on the head. It was only a year or more later that I found out, when he explained to me that his tribe finds it very funny indeed when someone is almost hit on the head.

As I looked at the goat-god, trying to sum up his sense of humour, he pretended to climb an invisible ladder. Then I realized that he thought that I was puzzled. He believed I had never seen a ladder before in my life. I decided to show him that our tribe has been making ladders, and good ladders at that, ever since the Egg, so I bounded up it in a few steps, swung over the top and slid down into the compound.

Then I remembered that I did not know how many belonged to his tribe and I looked around me in some fear. It was strange in there, I tell you, strange to be surrounded by all those killed trees with spikes at the top. I leaned against that wall of spikes and I shut my eyes and I thought of you, my own people, for one moment.

But then I had to look at the new strangeness. As far as I could see there were no other people in the compound. There was one hut at the far side, but such a complicated hut that it made you blink. It was not a hut built just for living in, surely, but a hut built to last for many, many years. And high above it a many-coloured cloth was flying, which later he taught me to call Flag.

Outside the hut was what he calls a table and what he calls a chair. A table is a sort of high wooden lap on which to place your bowl of food if you do not want to hold your bowl on your own lap. And a chair is for sitting on instead of sitting on the ground, because if you sit upon the ground you cannot reach the high wooden lap of the table. If you have a table you must have a chair. There are more complications with knives and forks, and cups and plates, but let it be simply understood for now that the eating ceremony of the goat-god is extremely difficult for aliens since it is a maze of taboos.

By now the goat-god stood beside me. He was tying the ladder so that if others arrived outside they could not pull it over. Evening was arriving quickly. He turned and pulled down Flag, with one hand raised to the side of his head. Then he moved to a raised platform, overlooking the sea. He gazed at the view for a moment, then he got down on his knees, clasped his hands, shut his eyes and muttered very quickly.

I decided to explore the hut. You should see inside the hut.

That was indeed something to see. One of the walls seemed to be all one shining tribute to the moon and sun and stars. They shone into my eyes. That wall was covered with wonderful things, made by men, but shining. Later I learned the names of the materials from which they were made – brass, silver, pewter, steel and glass. There were more than a hundred different things hanging from hooks or sitting on shelves – jars, tools, scissors, plates, barrels and many things for which we have no names. Each of those things had a most distinct and deliberate and interesting shape. To see one hundred objects you have never seen before, suddenly, all at one go, is both shocking and happy for the spirit.

Some chains were hanging on a hook. I touched them, the first time I had ever touched metal. At the same time I saw my face with terrible clarity in a special glass. The chains were cold upon my skin and the sight of the face made me jump with fright. The chains clanked against each other. I could not move, although I wanted to run.

A voice tore through my head – 'Poor Robinson Crusoe! God Save the King! All will be well!' Beside my face I saw a parrot sitting, its foot chained to a perch. Then the goat-god came in. He seemed displeased to find me in his hut.

'Ah, there you are,' he said. 'Not in here. Not here. Out, out. This is my place.'

He pushed me out of the hut and into the compound.

'Out here. You stay out here. This is your place. You lie down. Hey, I can't keep calling you *you*. Can't even give you a Christian name, seeing that you're certainly no kind of Christian. Not yet. I know, let's see, what day of the week is it?'

He turned to a group of tall poles on which thousands of notches had been cut. He ran his fingers down the notches and began to mark them off.

'Sunday, Monday, Tuesday, Wednesday, Thursday – right, that'll do, I call you Thursday. No, just a moment, it must be

Friday. So you'd better be Friday too. Yes. You – Friday. Because I saved you on a Friday. You Friday. Funny, I was shipwrecked on a Friday, too. Right, Friday, you sleep here.'

He pointed to me, then to the ground and then, while he still stood up, he pretended to sleep. When he indicated that I should sleep on the earth, I was very glad. Because I was tired and amazed almost to death. So I lay down upon the earth, which was not trick goat-god earth, but ordinary earth like we know. Just like this earth I now pat with my hand. I lay down and my head became dark.

That night I dreamed of my dead friends. While I was asleep I dreamed of the way they lived. But as I lay in my half-sleep, in the first light, I dreamed of the way they died. They died suddenly, like mosquitoes when you slap them on your thigh. I knew then that, if I was to live, I must be a very cunning mosquito.

When I sat up in the morning to taste the air, the first thing I saw was the barrel of that musket pointing at me from the hut. He must have been sitting up all night guarding himself from me.

CHAPTER FOUR

In Which I am Given My First Lessons in the Language of England

The goat-god walked out into that first morning of ours and looked at me for a time, musket under his arm. He smiled. I smiled in return. That seemed the right response, for he turned, went back into his hut and then emerged with food. The mixture I was offered for breakfast was enough to choke you just to think about it – it consisted of seeds and husks mixed up with the milk of goats. It had no spices, no richness and no subtlety. (I very soon managed to take over the cooking duties, which are confined to the women of his tribe.) But if the English food he offered was difficult to eat, the manner of the eating of this mess was entertaining for me.

Following his eating ritual I learned that it is proper to hold the bowl in the left hand and the beautiful shining thing called spoon in the right. The spoon should be tapped against the side of the bowl twice, to produce a satisfying ringing tone. The eater should then cough, raise his spoon to his mouth and take some food in. He may then chew and swallow, after which he should cough again, then tap his bowl twice, and so on. At the end of the eating, if you can force down all the mealy stuff without choking, you are rewarded by the sight of a blue pattern painted long ago on the inside of the bowl.

We completed that first breakfast and then, immediately, we were having our first language lesson. Now I had been dreading this moment. How many languages would I have to learn? I need not have worried. For while our tribe has one language for love, another for children, another for old people, another for cooking, another for hunting, another for fishing – the English tribe, to which the goat-god belonged, has only one language for everything. So you see, if they are very complicated in some ways, they are very simple in others. The lesson started like this, with myself learning by simple repetition.

'You – Friday.'

'Fri-day.'

He was amazed at that. He slapped on his thigh and sat forward.

'Yes, good, Friday.'

'Friday.'

I looked at him and made my face the shape of a question. I pointed my finger towards him.

'Friday?'

He shook his head.

'No.' He pointed to himself. He thought for a moment as if he were not sure which of his names to call himself.

'Me – Master.'

'Me Master?'

'No, no, no.'

He pointed to himself.

'Me Master.'

He pointed to me.

'Friday.'

He pointed to himself again.

'Master.'

Easy. I had it now and I locked those two names in my mind by repeating them, pointing at me and then at him and then at me and then at him and so on.

'Ah. Friday. Master. Friday. Master. Friday. Master.'

At this point I stopped calling him the goat-god to myself, and from now on in this story I will talk about him as Master. Master looked me up and down. He seemed pleased.

'You're sharp, lad, you're sharp,' he said. 'Maybe it won't

take too long to teach you English. We must work hard at it. It'll be very helpful in getting jobs done efficiently. And you'll be much better company than that parrot. Better start, I suppose.' He pointed to his head. 'Head, head.'

I thought that was not so good a word, and that I had a better one, so I shook my 'head'.

'Head, head,' he insisted.

I grinned, shook my 'head' once again. I was thinking of one of our tribe's words.

Master pointed at different parts of his body, demonstrating.

'Head. Nose. Mouth. Hand. Arm. Body. Leg. Foot.'

I realized that he was expecting to do nothing but teach. Perhaps he was hoping that we would only speak the words of his people and use none of ours. I could not allow that. If I was to learn his ways, he must learn ours. And I liked the sound of some of our words better. So I pointed at the same parts of my body and listed their best names.

'Baskra. Logglephan. Omra. Lashti. Clyserta. Clavara. Eegra. Dom.'

'Friday!'

'Master!'

He jabbed a bony red finger towards my head.

'Head,' he said. 'Head.'

'Baskra?'

'No, not bloody baskra. Head. Head.'

Master touched his own head, then mine. Then he raised his fist as if in anger. I cowered away, as if afraid. He lowered his fist, smiling, and then spoke.

'Friday. This is my island. This is Master's island and Master is an Englishman and so this island is a part of England and so we will speak English. English. Friday will speak English too. And you'll stop talking that black language of yours if I have to tear your tongue out by the roots.'

He was shouting very loudly. I thought he must be very ill.

He had probably been alone for many years. And to be alone for so long must make any man ill. That is what I thought at the time. You will see how far I was right and how far I was wrong, in that when he first came to the island he was not very well.

Master calmed himself. He had to calm himself because I kept very still and silent and relaxed all of my muscles to bring him to calmness. When he spoke again, his voice was much quieter.

'Start again, Friday. Friday.'

'Friday.'

'Master.'

'Master.'

'Head.'

'Bas—'

But he raised his fist against me again.

'Head. Head,' he shouted.

I tried my best to say it.

' 'Ed. 'Ed.'

The lesson continued. He was certainly not interested in learning any of our languages or special words. Since I was younger and my brain therefore more quick-moving than his, it was only courteous for me to learn his way of speaking first. By the end of the morning I knew many English names – Master, Friday, head, nose, mouth, arm, body, leg, foot, England, parrot, God, flag, eat, food.

We combined learning with other work. I remember another of those early lessons, one I particularly enjoyed. Master had taken me to an open space near a beach. He had planted many vegetables in straight lines and had built a small wooden hut in which to keep his digging tools safe from the rain. At first I found the idea of vegetables in straight lines so funny that I could hardly stand up. But I stopped laughing after I had been digging for a while. As we dug up fat root vegetables, Master taught me new words.

'Dig,' he said.

'Dig,' I replied.

He leaned on his spade. Sweat was running down his scarlet face. He gave a thin little whistle. I responded with a few selected jungle bird calls. His face smiled.

He whistled and said: 'Whistle.'

I imitated him. We had now agreed a teaching method and there was no stopping us.

We coughed and then said: 'Cough.'

We laughed and then said: 'Laugh.'

We pretended to cry and then said: 'Cry.'

We screamed and then said: 'Scream.'

And then we did it all over again, a good rhythm beginning to grow out of the list of words, his rhythm dragging a little maybe, but some really good screams and laughs coming in from him and some extra special bits of whistling from me – whistle, cough, laugh, cry, scream, it was becoming a chant and then all over again until I was dancing to the beat of this new song all over the vegetables in their lines and the birds were jumping out of the palm trees at the noise and I was moving down into the low crouch position of dance – and then he grabbed me by the arm and stopped me.

'That's enough, Friday, that's enough. Mustn't get carried away, must we? Mustn't forget what we're here for. To work and to learn.'

Master handed me a spade.

'Dig,' he said, 'Dig.'

'Dig dig,' I said. But I would rather have said dance if I had known that word. We began to dig, alongside each other. We used to dig the earth together in those days. Suddenly Master looked up and smiled, leaning on the top of his spade with his elbows.

'Friday is good,' he said, and clapped his hands.

'Master is good,' I said, and clapped my hands.

That was my first sentence in the English language.

CHAPTER FIVE

In Which I Learn the Meaning of Mine and Yours

Master began to fear me less and less. After a while he even began to leave his musket behind when we ventured beyond the stockade, although he wore his pistols at all times. At the same time, my fear of Master was shrinking. At first he had walked in all my dreams, his face a scarlet skull, his arms exploding muskets. Those nightmares stayed with me for some time, but I worked on them with cleansing exercises, and they gradually left me. There was the basic fear that Master might shoot me at any time. I faced that fear and said to myself: 'Why, any man may die at any time. That is fear not worth feeling.'

But once I had overcome my main fear of Master, he often seemed extremely funny to me. He was so serious about himself and the island. He was so serious about everything. He worried before he spoke, he worried about what he would say. He worried while he said it, and after he had said it, he worried about what he had said. He was so busy. And if there was nothing to be busy about on the island, he would invent business which had to be done. So funny. But when I laughed at him, he grew angry. I tried to keep my laughter to myself.

One of the funniest Master things was the way he dressed – in that pointed hat, that waistcoat, those enormous trousers and those fat shoes all made out of goatskin. To see him walking in that costume had astonished me at first, but now it seemed absurd, especially when he held above his head that furry sunshade to protect his head.

So it was for the sake of the joke that early one morning I

put on his outfit. It felt heavy on my shoulders and waist, and it itched mightily, but it had the strange effect of making me feel larger and stronger than usual, as if I could push over a monster if I met one. I sauntered down to the fishing pool, meeting no monsters on the way. I sat, huge and furry, on a rock, dropped in my line and began to order the fishes about, telling them to hurry up and bite the hook of the fisherman with fur. I smiled at my reflection in the water. That grey pointed head suited me. Suddenly I saw another face in the water beside mine and turned. I smiled at Master. He didn't laugh at my clothes joke. He had been supposed to laugh. Well, I like sharing jokes. What else can you do with a joke? But his face was screwed up. He held the musket in his right hand.

'Friday! Hat. Waistcoat. Trousers. Shoes. Sunshade.'

Language lesson. Repeat after me. Very well. I repeated that list and added the word 'Fish', showing him a large, almost transparent green fellow I had just caught.

'It's time for another lesson, Friday. A new kind of lesson.'

'Good,' I said, putting down my rod and turning away from the water and its bright wriggling. 'A new lesson. Good.'

'Today we will speak only in sentences. We have learned to speak in sentences, haven't we?'

'Good. We will speak in sentences. It is a fine day. Here is a green fish. My face is black. We will speak in sentences. Very good.'

'That is good. Now Friday, listen to this sentence. That hat is mine. And listen to this one. That waistcoat is mine.'

'What is *mine*?' I asked.

Master took a deep breath. He let it go. Then he took another, deeper breath, scratched his forehead and began.

'Listen, Friday. There are many things in the world. Some of these things are for everybody. There is the sky. The sky is for Master and Friday and everybody. There is the sea. The sea is for Master and Friday and everybody. But there are other things which are for some people, but not for everybody.'

I raised my eyes and opened my hands to show that I could understand the words he was using even if his general meaning escaped me. He continued.

'This island,' he said, 'it is for Master and Friday and nobody else. Its trees and its fruit and its animals are for Master and Friday and nobody else. And, most important, Friday, there are other things which are for one person only and for nobody else.'

This was strange talking. He was not joking. But his ideas became odder with each sentence. I had to stop him, so that I could work this out.

'What can be for one person only?' I asked. 'This is a riddle, Master. A moment. What is for one person only? A man's death? That is for him only? No, no, it is for the whole of his tribe also.'

Master felt a little anger which he showed by exposing his upper teeth.

'It is not a riddle. These trousers are for one person only. These trousers are for Master only. I can say: these trousers are mine.'

No, it was too peculiar to be funny. I asked him: 'These trousers are mine?'

'No,' he shouted. 'These breeches are *mine*. That loin-cloth you wear every day, that loin-cloth is yours. You – yours. Me – mine.'

Yes, now I could begin to understand darkly. Well, I could at least understand the linguistic point he was making.

'Ah,' I said. 'The trousers are yours. The loin-cloth is mine. Is that right, Master?'

He nodded and took another of those very deep breaths. He spoke to me very slowly and carefully, worrying over his words even more than usual.

'Very good. Now. That hat you are wearing on your head. That hat, Friday, is mine.'

I reached up and patted it with my hand. It felt pleasant.

'But the hat does not know it is yours. It fits Friday's head well, just the same as it fits the head of Master. Perhaps it is for Master and Friday and nobody else?'

What I said was true, for the hat sat most comfortably all round my skull. It had a job to do, to protect me from the sun. It was doing that job extremely well. A good hat. I reached up and patted it again.

'But it shouldn't be on Friday's head. That hat is for Master only.'

'Is there some magic in the hat, some magic that makes it for Master only?'

'That's it, Friday. Yes. There is magic in the hat. Master's magic.'

I had seen what his magic could do when it was angry. It had killed three of my friends on the beach. I tore the hat away from my head and threw it to Master. He put it on. I felt my hair with hands to make sure the magic hat had not torn away any of my scalp.

Master shouted again: 'And there is Master's magic in the waistcoat! And in the shoes! And the trousers!'

He did not need to tell me what to do. I pulled them all off as quickly as I could. What a lucky escape, I thought at the time. Master watched me, smiling. He collected the clothes as quickly as I dropped them.

When I had stripped to my loin-cloth, I dived in the fishing pool to wash away any wisps of magic that might be clinging to me from the clothes. As we walked back to the stockade so I could grill that green fish, Master explained further.

'You see, Friday, *mine* is a word full of magic. When I tell you that something is mine, it is very bad luck for you to touch it unless I take off the spell. Look at this. This goatskin sun-shade is mine. Don't touch it.'

I shook my head.

'Now I will take off the spell.'

He mumbled some words under his breath. I tried to hear the magic words but the only one I could understand was 'sun-shade'. Then he looked at me and smiled.

'I have taken the spell of mine off the sunshade, just for today, Friday. Now you may touch the sunshade.'

I made a face to show that I was not sure about that.

'Come on, touch the handle of the sunshade. It will not hurt you now. Take it from me.'

I took hold of the handle with my eyes shut. There was no pain.

'Hold it over my head as we walk home,' said Master.

I held it above him. He suddenly stopped and pushed the end of his musket under my nose.

'And Friday, this gun is mine. I have put the strongest spells of all on this gun and my pistols. They will kill men with black skins like Friday. But they will not hurt white men like Master. Look at it. This gun is mine.'

'Yes, Master, I know that.'

He was a strange creature. His eyes became brighter than usual when he talked about killing.

CHAPTER SIX

In Which the Story-Teller Takes a Well-earned Drink

'Friday' paused, squatted, extended his hands. A full gourd of palm-wine was passed to him. He relished it and smiled around him. It was customary in a long story to create such pauses. Listeners could be silent, or they could ask questions, or they could comment with short songs or stories of their own making. The doctor considered a long time, then decided that his question was ripe.

'This Master person, his mind was very ill. Did he talk such gibberish all the time?'

'The answer must be both yes and no. Most of the time he talked like that. But his nonsense had some kind of pattern to it, it wasn't random. When I questioned his beliefs, he became angry and told me that nearly all the people of his England island thought in the same way.'

Everybody laughed. An amazing island. The doctor managed to stop laughing and shook his head.

'Do you mean he claimed to come from a whole island full of people going around like this?'

The doctor acted out his point by walking jerkily among the people, glaring at them, snatching a doll here, a musical instrument there, and saying snappily: 'This is *mine*, this is *mine*.'

The game caught on and soon there were twenty or more of the tribe on their feet, strutting around, playing at being English. They called out to each other as they jerked around: 'This is *mine*. No, this is *mine*. That is *yours*.' They tickled each other and fell about with laughter.

'Friday' laughed too: 'Oh yes, I think England must be something like that. You have the idea. Now calm down.'

The game of England stopped and the 'Englishmen' sat down and concentrated on 'Friday' again.

'Master said that if you didn't understand the words mine and yours in England, you were either a bad man or a mad man and should be locked away in a dark hole.'

A girl asked: 'They lock people away in holes?'

'Oh yes. That is very important. Most of the English do as they are taught to do – that is they observe the taboos of mine and yours very religiously. But there are a few who do take things which are not for them. When a man does that, he is taken to a dark hole made out of stone. This is called a prison. A prison is a huge bad hut. It is full of bad men. And in this bad hut, the bad men are fed on bad food. They are shouted at and beaten and made to do things they do not want to do.'

'Who beats them?' asked the doctor.

'They are in the care of other bad men who are called jailers. These are frightening men of great strength.'

'Do the jailers live in the bad hut too?' asked the girl.

'Yes, most of the time. But the jailers are sometimes allowed out. And they are rewarded with gifts by the good men who do not live in the bad hut.'

The doctor was shocked, truly shocked. 'But if you hide a man in a bad place, away from good people, and away from the light – his mind will go bad. And if his mind rots away, the spirit will leave him. And then he can bring nothing but evil upon his own people.'

'Friday' nodded. 'You speak the truth. And I think the mind of that island, England, must be very ill.'

'Unless, of course, England does not exist, or only exists in the mind of Master.'

'We cannot prove it,' said the doctor. 'Anyway, the important thing is what a man does, not what we think he thinks.

So what did you do? What did you do to try to make this Master well again?'

'I allowed him to think he was teaching me. And at the same time, I tried to teach him.'

'Friday' put down his drink. He braced himself to resume the chanting of his story. The tribe smiled and edged closer to him. The musicians took up their instruments again and began to work.

CHAPTER SEVEN

In Which Master Denies the Banana and I am Taught the Religion of Trousers

He was such a busy teacher, Master. We are used to teachers who say nothing for days and nights on end. We are all taught to do one thing at a time – look at a leaf with your whole body and mind and spirit, catch a fish with your whole body and mind and spirit, touch a body with your whole body and mind and spirit – that is our way. But Master always wanted to be doing many many things at the same time. It is a wonder he did not tear himself in many pieces. Sometimes it seemed as if he had done so.

Even when we were out hunting pigs, he talked all the time. What a busy head, what a busy tongue! I tried to concentrate on holding my spear ready to throw at the first sight of a glistening snout, but his talk was so strange that I had to give up all thought of serious hunting.

He spoke of a one alone almighty God up in the sky. He spoke of a God who watched me all the time. This God lived on a cloud with his friends, many men and women with wings who played stringed instruments. These flying musicians, or angels, were good dead people. Although they were men and women, they did not make love at all, but were happy to make songs all day and night saying how good the one alone almighty God was. I thought that such songs, all the time, might prove boring to God, but Master said this was not so, that such praises were always pleasing to him. We all know people like that.

'Do the angels have nothing else to do?' I asked.

'Oh yes,' said Master. 'For they are God's army against the

36

forces of wickedness. They fight with flaming swords against the enemy.'

'Who is the enemy?'

'The hosts of Hell, under the command of Satan.'

'Ah.'

Master had told me about these hosts before. Satan is the chief devil of England. He is very tall and red in colour. He has large red wings and horns. He carries a fishing fork. His hut is called Hell and it is full of people like Friday who have broken mine and yours taboos or been cheeky to the God of England.

'Master,' I asked, 'if your God is almighty and has all the power, why does he not kill Satan now?'

'He could kill Satan now. If he wanted to. Of course he could. So he must have a very good reason for not killing him.'

'Perhaps he could kill Satan, but he is saving him up for last?'

That seemed possible, because Master had taught me that his God was very interested in revenge. I decided to show what I meant, so I took a deep breath to make myself bigger, like the God of England, and then I stamped around, wagging my finger at an imaginary Satan devil on the ground.

'You bad old Devil,' I shouted. 'You just wait down there. You watch what I do to the others. And when I've finished with them, I'll bring all my angels along with flaming swords and we'll do much worse to you. We shall push you on the ground and kick your head and hit you with our swords and you will feel sorry and call out and ask to be allowed to play a stringed instrument and sing my praises but I shall just kick you some more.'

Just then a piglet rushed through the clearing and I lost my way in the God versus Satan argument. Master fired, but he was not thinking clearly enough and the piglet was away.

'That's a very mighty God,' I said.

37

'Friday, you are very confused. But I think you may yet come to understand a little. There's so much for you to learn, so much to warn you about. For instance, just in case we ever return to England together, I must tell you that not all my people are God's men. Oh no, we have many heretics.'

'They do not like your God, Master?'

'Well they say they like God, and they honestly believe they believe in God. But their God is not the true God. Theirs is a strange and foreign God.'

'But you say there is only one true English God on your whole island.'

'Yes. But these heretics have invented their own God. They are called Roman Catholics, and they are very cunning, the Papist dogs.'

'Ah, they are dogs?'

'No, Friday, that was a metaphor. They are people, but they think like dogs. So I call them dogs.'

'The dogs we have are not cunning. But if these people have invented a naughty God, that is very bad.'

'Oh, that's not all. They worship the mother of God. They worship statues too. God doesn't like that at all. Statues upset him. And they worship an old man in Rome. They worship far too many things.'

What could that mean? I wanted to speak with him truly about my own people at that moment.

'Then the people of my island must be very bad people. We worship everything.'

He stopped and looked at me most carefully, making his blue eyes small.

'You have many gods, Friday?'

'Oh yes. We've got gods everywhere. Gods sitting by the fire, gods playing in the surf, gods riding on the backs of goats, gods hanging upside down from palm trees. Gods in our heads, we've got gods in our fingers, gods in our feet. The things

38

we make, the bowls and drums and spears – each one contains a god.'

We were walking down a slope and from the corner of my eye I saw a large hog lying asleep in the sun. I smiled at it as I raised my spear and killed it perfectly. But Master was horrified.

'Friday!' he yelled. 'You shouldn't stick a sitting pig.'

That was one of Master's sayings which I remembered and puzzled over but never understood. As I trussed up the hog, Master returned to the gods. He was very busily worrying over our gods, his mind scrambling about.

'Tell me, Friday, these gods of yours. What are they like?'

'All different.'

'Different shapes and sizes?'

'Oh yes. Every shape you can think of. Every size you can imagine.'

'Can you see these gods?'

'Some of them you can see. Some of the time. Some you can just hear. Especially the night-time gods.'

'But there are plenty of day-time gods too?'

'Oh yes, they're all around us now.'

Master clapped his hands like a trap closing on an animal. 'Then show me one,' he said.

That was easy. I walked over to a bunch of bananas, picked one and handed it to him. Banana. The word banana is one of the best English words I learned. And I think the tribe should use it sometimes. Anyway, Master looked at the banana, but he did not look at it with enough care and love.

'That's not a god. It's just a banana,' he said.

'It's just a god, too,' I said.

'But how can you worship a banana?'

He tossed the banana to me and I caught it.

'You can worship any way you like,' I told Master. 'So long as you mean it, the god won't mind how you do it.'

'But you *eat* bananas. How can you treat a god like that? Eating him?'

'If you eat him worshipfully, the god will be pleased.'

I showed him how by peeling the banana carefully, looking at it, taking a bite, chewing, swallowing and smiling. While I ate the banana I thought of nothing but the pleasure of eating the banana – its texture, its taste, its weight, its smell, its colour, its construction, its past, present and future and the satisfaction of my throat, stomach and bowels. All this was not enough to convince Master.

'All right,' he said. 'Show me another god.'

I pointed at him.

He smiled and shook his head.

'Ah, now you may think of me as a god. But you know, Friday, I'm not really a god at all.'

It is hard to teach an Englishman. But I am very obstinate and I persisted.

'To yourself,' I said, 'I think you are not yet a god. I don't think you worship yourself as you should. But still you are a god, whether you know it or not.'

It was strange, but whenever I told him anything serious, Master laughed. And of course whenever I made a joke, he took it extremely seriously and would want to debate it by the hour.

'How could anyone be a god and not know it?' he asked, but he did not stop for an answer. 'Show me one more god,' he demanded.

I pointed at myself. More laughter from Master.

'All right,' I said. 'What does your God look like?'

'Our God, Friday, is so great that he cannot be seen by mere men.'

'Too big to be seen?'

'Too great in every way.'

'Well, what would he look like if men had great eyes?'

Master thought about that one. He had to do something else while he thought, so he tapped one foot on the ground and scratched his hat with his left hand. He could never do just one simple thing at a time. A very busy man indeed.

'Let's see,' he said. 'God made us in his image. So if we could see him, he would look like a human being, I expect.'

'Like me, or like you?'

Master laughed.

'If I could see him,' he said, 'I suppose he'd look like me.' He smiled and patted me on the head. 'But if you could see him, perhaps he'd look like you. Only far greater, of course.'

'So your one single all alone God is really many gods?'

He stopped laughing.

'Well, perhaps he is one God who can take on many shapes.'

'Yes,' I said. 'And perhaps one of those shapes is the shape of a banana.'

He stood extremely still for about one second. Then he shouted: 'You can't believe in a banana! You can't believe in a banana!'

Then he put down his musket, clasped his hands and stared at the running clouds. His lips moved, but no sound came out of them. He was talking to God and his angel friends. The odd thing was that they did not seem to mind if he did all the talking. Suddenly he turned to me.

'Friday, my God has just honoured me by sending me a most important message.'

I was relieved. At least he was talking sensibly now. And his God might have been making my task a great deal easier by explaining away a few of Master's basic religious difficulties.

'Oh good. What does your God say?'

'He says that Friday must be saved straight away.'

'Saved?'

'Made ready so that if you die you will go to heaven and join the host of angels.'

'I can play a stringed instrument.'

'Don't be frivolous. You must be baptised.'

I thought it was some kind of rough Master joke as he pushed me in front of him down the slope and into the pool. I came up laughing and found that Master had jumped in beside me with all his furs on. Then he started to duck me. Of course I tried to duck him back, but that made him furious and he shouted very loudly about his father and a ghost and ducked me under some more until I shouted out:

'Oh Master, must I be drowned in order to be saved?'

He let go of me then. He began to climb out of the pool, water dripping like light from all over his wild goat clothes.

'Jesus has now washed away your sins,' he said to me. 'And now that you're a Christian, you will dress like a Christian.'

That is how I became a Christian and was made to wear trousers.

CHAPTER EIGHT

In Which I am Taught Some Sad and Funny Things About England

Every evening, as the sun began to spread itself across the sea, I would prepare a great bowl of drink. It was a mixture of our own palm wine, various fruit juices, spices and herbs. But at the heart of it lay always a small but burning portion of a liquid called rum. Master had salvaged some round wooden boxes of this substance from the great boat on which he was wrecked. Before that boat broke on the rocks it was still possible to climb aboard it and bring many useful things ashore. Now rum is not exactly useful, but Master felt for it a great concern and affection. He said it gave 'a kick' to his evening drinks. And when he was greatly worried or troubled, he would sometimes drink rum on its own. Then he would become drunk in an unhappy way, but after a time he would be forced to sleep.

But it was rare for Master to drink that much. Most evenings he would climb into his rocking chair on the balcony overlooking the small silver bay and he would watch the sun go down. And I would bring the drink for him and also a tray with a snack of fruit or fish or finely chopped vegetables, arranged in patterns which pleased his eye even if he did not understand what each pattern was saying. I would sit beside him, dangling my legs from the balcony and sipping palm wine from a coconut shell as he drank from a shining cup of silver. After our first drink, Master would usually talk about England.

He explained to me that England is a great island. It is even greater, or so he claimed, than Friday's island. Our island, measured by the walking of a man, is two days and two nights long and half a day wide. But England island is fifty days and

43

nights long, or perhaps, Master had not walked it himself, forty days and nights. Or twenty days and nights upon a horse. A horse? I am sorry, I will explain horses.

A horse, as I understand from Master, is an animal as big as ten pigs, with a long hairy tail and a nose twice as high as the nose of a goat. A horse can carry a man on his back for many miles and for many hours. Or the horse can pull a wooden hut upon wheels, and four people may sit in that hut. It may rain, but they will be covered by the roof of their hut on wheels as they travel about their island. The horse has not been taught by God that he must carry men and pull huts on wheels. So he has to be taught by men.

One night Master drew me a horse with his writing tool, but I laughed so much that he tore it up.

I said to him: 'Master, if I am in England, and I want a horse to carry me, do I just walk into the jungle and choose a horse and say come with me and I will teach you to carry me and pull my hut on wheels?'

'England has no jungles.'

I stopped myself laughing. I was going to have to start drawing my picture of England in my head all over again.

'But Master, every island has a jungle.'

'Not England. England has many trees, but no jungle.'

'But a jungle is many trees.'

He poured himself another drink, sipped, stood up, then paced backwards and forwards along the balcony.

'No. A jungle is hot and wet. England is cold and wet. We have woods, not jungles. The woods are too cold for monkeys, too cold for parrots, and too cold to bear fruit.'

'Then where do the people of England find their bananas?'

'You're absurd Friday! You're impossible! Why do you always have to bring everything back to bananas? Why can't you be serious?'

'I'm serious. I'm serious about bananas. Where do the English people find their bananas?'

44

'There are no bananas in England.'

That was so absurd that I slapped my arms and legs and did a laughing dance around the compound until the tears were running well. When my laughter had all gone, my mood changed quickly as I realised what it must mean to have no bananas at all.

So I cried out: 'Poor England!' But then I had to laugh again.

'Friday! I forbid you to laugh at England.'

'I am sorry, Master.'

'There is nothing funny about England.'

'But no bananas! Your island must be very poor.'

'No, England is very rich. We have many things which Friday's island does not have.'

'You have horses pulling huts on wheels?'

'Horses and coaches, we do indeed. And many other things besides, many, many things.'

'What else?'

'Thousands of things. I don't know where to start.'

'Tell me something. Something which is special for England.'

'Well, let's see. The Navy. Yes the Navy is very special for England. We have the finest navy in the world.'

'Navy?'

'A navy is many boats.'

'Friday's island has many boats. Friday came to Master's island with the Friday navy. But the navy was in a bad storm, otherwise I could show you how fine our boats are.'

'But that's a totally different thing. Friday's navy only fishes. England's navy does not fish at all.'

'Then what can navy boats be for?'

'Our navy boats, I mean, the ships of England's navy fight with the ships of other navies. For my island is such a great island that greedy men sail for many days across the sea to try to take it with guns. But we are a brave island too, and we meet them with guns. And so far, thanks to the help of God

Almighty, and the bold example of our monarchs and leaders, we have always driven them away from our shores.'

'Oh, we have the same trouble. Tribes sometimes travel over the sea to Friday's island to take things.'

'Ah. So you call the men of your tribe together, take up your spears and go and fight the invaders?'

'That would be discourteous. Mostly they call on our island for food or water on their long journeys. So we give them what they need. There is plenty on Friday's island, there is always plenty. Sometimes – only once in Friday's lifetime – a bad tribe will come to kill the men and take the women away.'

'Yes! And then you kill?'

'In the old days, we did killings. Now we have different ways. The one time I have seen this it was like this. We saw the bad tribe coming with many warriors. We left our huts and hid our children in a safe place which I am not allowed to tell even to you. Then we hid until nightfall. When it was dark we all put on robes and masks which shine in the night. Then we haunted the bad tribe like ghosts, with appearances and disappearances and calling and tricks of all kinds. They were so frightened they paddled away across the ocean hardly touching the water. I remember that time. We tell that story very often and act out the ghost tricks in our dancing. There are fine costumes.'

It was now Master's turn to laugh. My turn to frown.

'All right, Master. You have a killing navy and Friday's island has a fishing navy. But what else do you have that we do not have?'

He scratched his beard to announce that he was just about to give birth to a new thought.

'England has a Parliament,' he said. 'That is a great hut where men talk about what the people of England should be told to do and what to do to the people of England if they are disobedient.'

'Oh, we have a great meeting hut, too,' I said. 'We go there to hear stories and dance and decide what we should do.'

'A great hut indeed,' said Master. 'How great would you say your meeting hut is?'

'It is a hut big enough for all the tribe to dance in. Is your Parliament that big?'

He did not answer. He drank some more. He scratched for a little while. He chewed a sweet root.

'I'll tell you something England has that Friday's island lacks,' he said at last. 'Coal.'

'Coal?'

'Coal.'

'Is coal good?'

He held out his shining cup for more and I filled it.

'Oh, coal is very good,' he said.

'Please explain coal.'

'Coal is black rock deep under the ground. Men dig it up out of the ground. Then it is sold to other men.'

'And the men who do not dig the coal, they eat the coal?'

'No. They burn it.'

'Ah. And then they eat it?'

'No. The coal burns very slowly and gives great heat in the huts of the people. And it is good for cooking meat. Because it burns more slowly than wood and gives more heat. And mine is a cold island.'

'Poor England,' I said. 'I would rather have a warm island with no coal and lots of bananas.'

But I don't think he heard me. He was staring at the stars as they appeared to us. He was always interested in the stars after his second or third drink.

'It is quite possible,' he said very slowly, 'quite possible that the stars themselves are made of coal.'

He shut his eyes and smiled, as if encouraged by this thought.

CHAPTER NINE

In Which I Learn that Winning Is Both Important and Unimportant

There lay, at this time, a light sort of peace between Master and myself. When I had first met him, his walking pace had been very fast, as if he were being pursued. Gradually I had managed to slow his walking until it was more appropriate to the island's warmth. I taught him this lesson not by talking, but with music, by humming aloud as we pushed our way along the island's paths. Without thinking, without worrying, his footsteps adapted to the tempo of my humming.

It was usual in the mornings for me to wake him with some guava juice and some un-English breakfast. But one day he was the first to wake, and I cleared my eyes to find him looking more excited than usual – blue eyes round like wet blue suns.

'I've remembered another thing England has that Friday's island hasn't got,' he said all in one breath, and so quickly that I had to motion him to slow down his enthusiasm. Half-awake as I was, I had heard the sentence as a single word. He repeated himself, and added:

'That thing is Sport.'

Dragging myself to my feet and pulling on my compulsory Christians (as I called them to myself – he called them trousers), I managed to ask the expected question:

'Master, what is this Sport?'

As we walked to the beach where we were to make Sport together, he explained. Sport, he said, was war without weapons and battles without bloodshed. But Sport was also more than that. It involved values like chivalry and sportsmanship. So while Sport was competition – like a battle – it should also be a battle in which every courtesy should be extended to the enemy, even to the extent of giving him the advantage. This did not sound very sensible to me, and I said so.

'Well, Friday, I'm not surprised. These are complicated beliefs and it takes many years in a special school to learn them. We have special schools in order to train our leaders to lead us.'

'And they learn to kill in the schools too? So they can go in the killing navy of England?'

'Yes, but that is not Sport, that is War. You see, Friday, Sport is a cut-throat competition in which no throats are cut.'

He seemed very pleased about saying that. So I clapped my hands to keep the conversation on a cheerful level. He repeated the cut-throat sentence. I still did not understand, but of course we have no special schools. We have no schools at all.

Master was determined to show me the nature of Sport. It was, he said, less important than Christianity, but nevertheless essential to England. Preparations for Sport began. I prepared about a hundred bamboo poles with rags on their tops and we set these along the beach in two lines. Across the two end bamboos we draped a liana.

'The winning post,' said Master. 'The winning post for the running race.'

We walked back down the beach towards the first pair of sticks. Master drew a line between them on the sand. He removed his waistcoat.

'This is the first kind of Sport I shall show you,' he said. 'We will run what is called a race. I will say ready, steady, go. And when I say go, we will both run between the lines of flags, towards those posts. And then we'll see who is the winner.'

'Winner?' I asked.

'The best runner,' he said, and started to crouch down on one knee, staring at the winning post.

'Just a moment,' I said.

He stood upright. I could see annoyance gathering between his eyes.

'When you say the best runner,' I said, 'do you mean the fastest runner?'

'Yes ...' But then he thought again. 'Well, the important thing is not whether you win or lose.'

'Then what is important?'

'The important thing is how you play. The important thing is *how* you run.'

'Good. I see. I understand.'

'I should hope so,' he said. 'Now do like me.'

We both went into that funny crouch position.

'Right?' said Master. 'Ready, steady, go!'

He moved very fast and with a great deal of work by all the parts of his body, his neck stretched back and his legs in their compulsory Christians leaping high off the sand and almost tripping with their anxious movements. I did a floating run, as at our dances when a runner circles round the tribe. Of course he reached the winning liana first, then he collapsed, panting in a heap. He looked up at me angrily as I stood over him.

'You let me win,' he said. 'You weren't trying.'

'You won?' I asked.

'I got here first.'

'But you said the important thing is how you run. I ran very beautifully. I enjoyed every step along the sand. My body was moving harmoniously. The breeze felt right along my skin. But you did not seem to like the running. Your legs were jerking. Your body was not happy. And listen to what your breathing is saying. Your breathing is not saying: thank you, that was good running. Your breathing says: Hey – that hurt – what do you think – you're doing to me!'

He climbed to his feet, still breathing with difficulty.

'Friday – you never went – to a sportsmanship school. Perhaps – that view of Sport – is too sophisticated. Forget what I said before. The important thing is to win. The next event will be the swimming race. You can swim, Friday?'

'Only in the water,' I said, and walked towards the sea. Soon we were balancing on a rock perched over the waves. Master pointed to a rock out in the bay, not far. We were to swim out to it and that would be the swimming race. Ready, steady, go again, and we splashed in. Master's swimming, like his running, was very busy and he splashed and spouted a lot. I dived underneath him, then did a water-leap over him until he shouted to me to get out of his way. Then I decided that if fast swimming was the way of Sport, I would go very fast, so I let my arms and legs carry me along the surface, on and on, forgetting about the rock, just absorbed in the idea of fast swimming, faster, faster, and Master was shouting that I had passed the rock. That was all right, I thought, what rock, I am doing fast swimming now. Then the voice of Master began to sound frightened, as if I might be trying to swim away from the island and escape him.

'It's a race to the rock, not to the bloody horizon! Friday, don't leave me! Friday!'

So of course I turned and swam back to him. Both of us reached the rock at exactly the same time and hauled ourselves up on to it.

Master said: 'Well, you did go a bit off course, but we'll call it a draw.'

A draw is what happens in Sport when both sportsmen do as well as each other. Master assured me that I could be well pleased with a draw.

The next Sport we tried was Soccer Football. This needed more preparation. We had to build two goals for a start. A goal is three poles tied together with lianas and backed with a fishing net. A ball had to be made of rolled-up cloth and leather. A pitch had to be marked out in the sand. And then Master told me to sit down and he spent the first part of the afternoon explaining to me the many things which I should not do in Soccer Football and what he would be allowed to do if I did these things. He explained that Soccer Football teams always wear different coloured shirts so that they will not become muddled up with each other. Master was blue shirt and I was red. We faced each other in the middle of the sand pitch.

'Remember now,' said Master. 'It's not how you play, but whether you can get that ball into that goal. And you mustn't touch the ball with your hands, right?'

I put my hands behind my back and clasped them so they would understand this prohibition.

'No hands,' I said.

'I will kick off,' said Master.

'Good. Ready, steady, go!'

Master kicked the ball, a little kick, pushing the ball next to my left foot. I stood to one side. Master pushed past and chased the ball, giving it small kicks all along the side of the pitch, running all the way down to my goal and then, when he was within an arm's length of my goal, kicking it in. He jumped in the air and came down again. Then he turned and saw that I was still standing at the centre of the pitch. He picked up the ball under his arm and ran back to me, seeming to be angry.

'That's one goal to me,' he shouted. 'But why didn't you try to stop me? You're meant to stop me.'

I decided to be chivalrous and sportsmanlike and explain at least part of my purposes.

'I am playing this game very carefully, Master. I have a plan so that I may win. The first part of the plan is to let you wear yourself out by much running and effort. This part of the plan is nearly complete.'

He looked at me suspiciously. My chivalry did not seem to please him.

'Your kick-off,' he said. 'What is the second part of your plan?'

But I had told him enough already. I gave him a ready, steady, go and then, after concentrating until all my purposes became one thing, I did it. I kicked the ball. The ball flew in a perfect curve from the centre over the footprinted sand of the pitch and hit the netting of Master's goal about half-way up. Master seemed unable to believe that I had scored. His mouth was open for a moment. Then he ran to retrieve the ball. Back to the centre he came, puffing more than ever.

'One all, I suppose,' he said. 'But that was, I'd say, a combination of brute strength and very good luck.'

I thought it only sportsmanlike to explain my kick.

'No, not really. I concentrated one part of my spirit in my right foot, one part of my spirit in the ball and one part of my spirit in the goal. And then I drew the three parts of my spirit together.'

Master did not seem to like that.

'Oh, you did, did you? Look, this is Sport, not Religion. I don't pray to God over a football match. If I did, no doubt he'd pack my goal-mouth with arch-angels. So none of your heathen magic. You're a Christian now. Play football like a Christian. And remember, no hands. My kick-off now.'

I stepped back. Master began to run with little kicks again. He tried to kick it over my head. So I jumped up and caught the ball between my teeth. Then I ran around Master, twice, down the pitch and dropped the ball in his goal. But this time he was really angry. He grabbed my shoulder and turned me round.

'It's football, not teethball,' he shouted.

'It's two goals to one,' I said. 'Two to one.'

'That's not a goal. No teeth.'

'You never said anything about teeth. You talked to me all afternoon about what I could do and couldn't do. But you never told my teeth they could not play.'

'It's obvious, isn't it?'

He pushed his face close to mine. I did not step away, but stared into his eyes, shifted from foot to foot and stuck out my chin. I was angry at his spoiling my soccer football.

'Where's the rule?' I shouted.

'It's common sense.'

'What's common sense?'

'Don't be silly, Friday.'

'Don't tell me common sense. There's no rule against teeth.'

'It's never been done!'

'You're making up new rules, because you're losing.'

'Look, you're asking for—'

'I'm asking for what?'

We were not friends at that moment. But suddenly both of us seemed to quieten, and at the moment both of us stepped back. Master walked round in a circle before saying:

'All right, Friday. The goal stands. I think it's time for the awards.'

We had prepared two boxes on the sand before the Sport began. One was twice as high as the other. Master stood on the higher box, I stood on the lower, holding a silver cup ready.

'First the award for the winner of the running race,' he announced. 'First, Master. Second, Friday.'

I gave him the cup, which he took with a nod and held proudly above his head.

'And now,' he said, 'my national anthem. After the presentation, we have to sing the winner's national anthem. You know the one I taught you, God Save? Right.'

We sang God Save our Gracious King, Long Live our Noble King, God Save the King. That was soon over. Then I jumped up on the upper platform beside Master for the drawn award for the swimming in the water race – equal first, Master and Friday. Both of us clutched the cup. We had to sing our anthems at the same time. While he sang his God Save I sang a swimming anthem I made up as I went along:

54

> 'Oh, swimming in the water
> is good, good, good.
> Swimming in the water.
> The water is a woman
> So you plunge your body in
> And then you draw it out again,
> And then you plunge it a little deeper.
> The water is a woman—'

But Master interrupted by telling me my anthem was not appropriate to a Sports ceremony. It was time for the football award, so I stood alone on the upper platform.

'And now,' I said, 'the glorious award for the great football battle without bloodshed and no hands. The score: Friday — two goals. Master — one.' I received the cup from Master. 'Thank you, England. And now the football national anthem of Friday.'

Master stood at attention, and I began to sing:

> 'Let me tell you of a war
> In which there was no fighting.
> Let me tell you of a battle
> In which there was no hurting.
> Victory did not matter at all
> It did not matter.
> And yet nothing mattered but the victory.
> How you fought was the important thing,
> And yet how you fought was not important at all.
> Let me tell you of the triumph of Friday
> In the great war of football . . .'

I kept singing in that way for as long as I could. Master gradually stopped standing stiffly and sat down, on the lower box. He did not seem very pleased with Sport.

CHAPTER TEN

In Which an Illness Is Found in the Tribe

'. . . It was a very fine triumph for Friday
in the great war of football!'

Carried away by the oddness of the story, the tribe broke in
with laughter, some reaching out to clap 'Friday' on the back as
he squatted for a brief rest. But the boy who had helped to
serve the drinks, a serious and slim boy in his mid-teens, was
so excited that he stood up and raised his hand for silence.
Respect did not go with years in the tribe, anyone was entitled
to speak.

The boy said: 'Perhaps there are some good things about
this Master person.'

The doctor responded automatically with one of the old sayings: 'When meat goes bad, it becomes poison.'

The boy groaned, and so did several others. 'That is an old
saying. Well, some of the old sayings are still useful, but that
one is so obvious that it would be good to send it over the sea. A
man is not just so much meat. There is more to a man than his
meat. Sayings like yours just stop people thinking.'

The doctor nodded. The attack was fair.

'I am wrong. You are right,' he acknowledged. He tried to
reclaim a little authority by adding: 'The young know everything. So tell us, what is good about this Master?'

The boy did not want to appear foolish, so he tensed his
hands and face a while before answering.

'Well, perhaps this idea of Sport is good. Perhaps running
against each other would be good.'

An old woman laughed.

'Why run against each other?' she asked. 'Why not run together?'

'Yes,' said the doctor. 'Why not run with each other, as we have always done? If one falls over the others are nearby to pick up the fallen one. The tribe runs together.'

'No, listen to me,' said the boy. 'Suppose that every year our whole tribe should meet together on the white beach. We would stand in a line on the sand. Then there would be a signal, and then we would all run to the other end of the beach. And the one who ran the fastest, he would receive a prize.'

Now the whole tribe was laughing. Two of them were repeating the absurd idea to friends who had missed the joke because of taking a short nap in the story pause. The doctor recovered first.

'What sort of prize?'

'A pig, perhaps.'

The old woman said: 'Why run for a pig? The pigs lie around all day in their compound just outside the hut. If you want some pork, there it is. Go and take a pig and slaughter it and cook it and share it.'

'Perhaps a prize is not so important,' said the boy. He was determined to persuade the tribe to give Sport a chance. 'It would be good, you see, to find out which of the tribe could run the fastest. He could be paid some honour by the tribe. He could be called the Runner.'

'Just as you like,' said the doctor. 'We will call you the Runner. Just like that. We will call you any name we choose. And you won't have to bother arranging the tribe in a line on the white beach. Is that all right, Runner?'

'I am not the Runner,' said the boy growing angry. 'But I would really like to know who is the fastest. And it would be good for the tribe. We would all practise running. And so we would move more quickly when we are out hunting.'

By now the boy was stamping his palm with his fist to

emphasize his argument. The doctor put his head on one side and made a quick diagnosis. He looked around the hut and beckoned to the young girl who had helped the boy to carry the gourd. She walked over to him.

'I think this boy is not very well,' said the doctor. 'Will you take him to his hut and make him better?'

The girl smiled and took the boy's hand. He tried to shake her off, but she held tight. As he started to protest that there was nothing the matter with him, she placed his hand on her bare breast.

'You are not very well,' said the doctor, smiling. 'Come back when she has made you better.'

The boy smiled, and allowed himself to be led out of the hut as the tribe laughed and clapped their hands.

'Friday' stood up to resume his narrative.

'Master would have recommended a tougher cure than that,' he said.

CHAPTER ELEVEN

In Which I Become Master and Master Becomes God

You might think, to hear me singing this story, that all my time on the island was spent in thinking about Master or in arguing with him. Of course not. Most of my time I was thinking of many other things – the changes in the sky, the categories of leaf-smells, variations in water-patterns, the behaviour of animals, the music of my body and, most of all, of you, my own people. It only seems that Master dominated my mind because I am forcing my story to stare at him. And I am doing that because, when I have finished singing, we must all decide what is to happen to Master.

There was always a space between myself and Master. But, after some time, that space became a warmer and warmer place. Master was still tight and tense in his muscles, especially the muscles of his neck, but his muscles did not grow tauter when I appeared. An odd kind of friendship began to grow. But it was suddenly stricken with a blight and how that happened, I will tell you now.

I returned to the compound one morning with a dead pelican slung over my shoulder after a good morning with my bow and arrows. I was pleased with myself as I climbed up the ladder, the weight of the bird bumping against my shoulders, my saliva already running at the thought of the well-baked flesh. In my mind I was beginning to select and prepare vegetables. I stopped at the top of the stockade and stared down, horrified.

Master was crouching down in the compound. He had taken his shirt off. This was rare. Even in the greatest heat he only removed his shirt to wash it. The skin of his torso was so white it made you blink. But there were also little long streaks of red across his prominent spine. In one hand he held a small branch with spread twigs at the end. He was twisting his arm into the air above his shoulder and beating his own back. When he realized I was there, Master started, then threw the branch away from him. I climbed down the ladder and waited for him to speak. He darted his head around like a bird looking for food, found his shirt, pulled it on clumsily, but still did not look at me. I fetched a knife, squatted on the ground and cut out the entrails of the pelican, but still he did not look at me, although his face was troubled. I enclosed the pelican most carefully in clay and set it in the oven all ready to bake. Master sat upon the ground hugging his knees. He seemed to want silence and nothing but silence. I thought that I should leave him alone, but I could not leave him there, looking so dangerous, without speaking to him.

'I've got a pelican ready for baking,' I said. 'Any special vegetables, you'd like with it?'

He nodded to me.

'I don't know,' he said. 'I'm not very hungry.'

'Is your stomach sick?'

'Yes, it feels sick.'

'Ah, I have some berries which will make you better within an hour. I'll just go and pick them, mash them up with goat's milk. Tastes marvellous, but it does you good.'

I started to climb the ladder but he called me back.

'I'm not ill,' he said.

'What is it, Master? Should I not have come back? Your eyes are very angry.'

'No, I'm not angry. Well, I'm not angry with you, Friday.'

'Are you angry with that branch?'

'Is that a joke?'

'Only if you want a joke, Master.'

'No, Friday, I can't bear a joke today. Friday, I must tell

you that God is very angry with me. And so, you see, I am very angry with myself.'

'But that's serious, Master. Are you sure that God really feels that way? Has God been talking to you again? Or did he send a sign of some sort?'

'I had a dream, Friday.'

'Oh, but that's good. A dream about God is always lucky. Whether he was angry or happy in the dream, that does not signify. Any God dream is very lucky. Everybody knows that. Now just be grateful for that dream and relax your neck and I will make that berry and goat's milk drink for you and it will be a lovely day for Master and Friday, no trouble.'

'Friday. Don't try to tell me what I was dreaming. This was not a God dream. It was a flesh dream. It was a dream about a woman. About the body of a woman.'

'Oh, a love dream? God would not send you a love dream if he was angry with you. We all need love dreams now and then, especially when we have no women.'

'Not love,' said Master. 'It was not love, but lust. And in this dream I used that woman. Like an animal.'

'You killed her? You ate her, maybe? Oh, that dream is not so unlucky either. If I remember correctly the eating a woman dream has a meaning which is to do with safe travel.'

'I did not eat her. I copulated with her.'

'That's a very lucky dream.'

'No.'

'Why? Couldn't she do it well? Didn't you both enjoy your copulation?'

He looked at me, and the blue of his eye centres was surrounded by thin, jagged red lines.

'Oh, I was very happy,' he said. 'Happy. Until I woke up. And then I was ashamed. I felt unclean. And I knew God was angry. And so I broke that branch off a tree. And when you arrived I was beating my back with the branch. So that God might forgive me.'

I almost asked him if the tree was not angry with him for breaking off part of it for such a purpose. But I remembered that the English tribe do not understand that each tree is a world with its own life and inhabitants. And I did not want to waste time in a long discussion about such an issue, when I should be finding out the nature of the sickness which was forcing him to beat himself. I wanted to make him better. Also I did not want to catch that sickness and begin beating myself.

'I don't think God is angry with you,' I said. 'I am sometimes angry, Master, if somebody hurts me. But you have not hurt your God at all.'

'He is your God too, Friday. He is everyone's God. He is God for all the world.'

'Yes, of course. But you have not hurt him, anyway. You have only hurt your back. Let me wash those wounds.'

'Leave them,' he said.

'Now that would be bad,' I said. 'If we should leave them your blood will become bad.'

I insisted. He knew I was right, so he reluctantly removed his shirt again. I washed his thin wounds with rum and then bound them with strips of cloth. When I had finished, he said 'Thank you.' Then he stood up and began to walk up and down in the compound.

'I must teach you the meaning of what you have seen me doing here this morning.'

'Yes, please teach me,' I said. 'I would like to learn. And I would like to help.'

'Friday. I have hurt God. Because every time we surrender to the temptations of the flesh, the agony of Jesus on the Cross is increased one hundredfold.'

'Temptations of the flesh?'

'Pleasures that we should not have, Friday. Bad pleasures,

62

like when you touch yourself down there. Yes. I have stopped you doing that because that is a bad pleasure, that is a temptation of the flesh. And every time you touch that for pleasure, it hurts Jesus upon the Cross.'

'Why?'

'Because he bears our sins. He takes them upon himself.'

'And our sins hurt him?'

'He is in great pain, Friday.'

'And he takes all our badness?'

'Yes.'

'And yet he is not bad at all.'

'Not at all. He is entirely good.'

You see the God of England is a very difficult person to understand and harder to live with. I will not explain all of this God's demands, or how he appoints warrior-doctors called bishops or how God insists that he must have a fine meeting hut in every settlement in England. But I will say briefly that there are many different kinds of sins or bad things which God does not like. Many of these sins are not bad things with us. For example, Master said that it is not a sin for a man to shit, because a man must shit. But it is a sin for a man to take pleasure in shitting. Likewise it is not a sin for a man to copulate with a woman with whom he has performed various rituals in one of the English God huts. But it would be a sin for the same man to copulate with the same woman without those rituals. And another sin for him to copulate with anyone else. And this Jesus who is also the English God, he did not copulate at all, although he lived for thirty-three years, he did not copulate once. I asked Master if Jesus ever shit, but he became angry and would not answer. Yes, it is all extremely hard to follow. I never really understood it all.

Anyway, each one of these sins is supposed to hurt Jesus on the Cross. Jesus was God you understand, but he was also a man sent by God to tell good stories to the people. But cruel people do not like good stories. So they took him and killed him upon this Cross. A cross is two big pieces of wood, fixed like this, and standing in the ground. They used to nail people to these crosses. They used to leave people hanging on these crosses till they died. Many, many people were nailed to such crosses and Jesus was one of them. Yes, it is hard to believe. When Master first told me about people being nailed to crosses, I vomited up my food. He seemed surprised and tried to explain to me that in some way the Cross was beautiful. No.

Let us return to the day on which Master beat his own back. I asked him once more that he should help me to understand. I said:

'Show me, Master. Pretend that you are God. And pretend that I am Master.'

'I'll do no such thing,' he said. 'Pretending to be God is wrong. And you pretending to be me – well, that's absurd.'

I explained that among my own people it is customary to understand things by acting them out, taking the parts of gods, women, men, children, animals, waters, trees and so on, with costumes and masks and music and feasting. That is one reason why I tell you so much of the conversations that I had with Master, so that the tribe can act out this story in the years to come. I told him that I would never understand about God and sin and love dreams if he did not show me. His mind altered slowly.

'All right, Friday,' he said. 'You must be taught. You are now – Master.'

I stood very still, trying to think my body into a Master shape. Master climbed up the ladder and made himself comfortable on the platform of the stockade. He looked down upon me and he smiled at me.

'You are Master,' he said. 'And I am God. And I am watching over you always.'

Up and down the compound I walked, trying to hold my

head like Master and move my arms and legs in the English fashion. This takes some concentration, as you have to convey a stiffness to each particular part of your body and limbs. I tried to imagine the inside of his mind. When I shut my eyes it seemed to be like the inside of his hut, cluttered with hundreds of shining objects, most of which were strange to me and whose functions I could not guess.

'I am poor Master,' I said. 'I have been alone for many many years. I feel tired, God.'

I stretched my arms and yawned.

'I am going to bed.'

I lay down on the ground.

'I go to bed alone. Good night, God.'

I half-shut my eyes. There was no word from Master/God. I looked up at him. He was hunched up. He looked very sad to see himself acted. Then he pulled back his shoulders and took a deep breath as if he was God.

'Good night, poor Robinson Crusoe,' he said.

I shut my eyes and curled up, pretending to snore gently. No word came to me from God. I sat up.

'You must tell me the dream, or I cannot dream it,' I said.

'But it was a wicked dream.'

'You must tell me or I cannot understand what is wicked.'

'I will tell you.'

I lay down again and closed my eyes once more. The voice of Master/God began. He seemed to be finding difficulty in making his words with his tongue.

'I dreamed a dream. And in that dream a woman came to me and touched my skin.'

I acted Master's dream, touching my own skin delicately without opening my eyes.

'She laid her head upon my breast. She touched my ears.'

I touched my own ears as if I had never touched them before. I pretended that my fingers were the fingers of a woman.

'I said: "Why? Why?" She said: "Because your ears are beautiful."'

I pretended to be talking in my sleep and said:

'Why? Why?' Then I lightened my voice to become the woman and said: 'Because your ears are beautiful.'

'Her clothes, she wore clothes, but they had no more substance than moonlight,' said Master, his voice tighter than before. 'Her body moved over my body like waves over the sand . . .'

I let my body move as if responding to the waves of the ocean and I felt the goodness of the movement running hot through my thighs and genitals.

'I began to jabber and thrust with love.'

I tossed my body, making love to the air and gabbling any nonsense which came into my head. The words were flying from my mouth. I could feel the joy mounting in my body.

Suddenly Master shouted: 'Stop it! Stop it, Friday! Stop it immediately!'

I sat up, quickly, angry to be interrupted.

'Well, what happened next?' I asked. 'I thought you were going to show me. Didn't you finish the copulation?'

'What happened next was that I woke up,' said Master. 'I woke up and said to God: "God, I am vile. Take my life, for there is no health in me."'

'All right,' I said. 'God, I am vile. Take my life, for there is—'

But Master interrupted me again, raging:

'And then God said to me: "Yes, you are a creature of vileness. A night-monster. A scarlet snake. Take that branch and chastise thy own back that thou mayest sin no more."'

That didn't sound right to me. I looked at Master to make sure he was not joking.

'God said that?' I asked, and then stood up.

Master calmed down very suddenly indeed.

'Well, something like that,' he said.

'I see – so you took the branch off the tree?'

'I am God's servant.'

Now I could see it all. I could see his sickness. A simple sickness with an extremely simple cure. Of course you guessed it. Only a child would not understand.

'Oh, but Master, you're not alone on this island. I'm here. If you'd told me that you needed loving, I would have helped you.'

He looked at me, puzzled.

'Helped me?'

'I have a body too,' I said. 'I am a loving man.'

Master stood there a long time, the tension in his body doubling, the redness of his face turning to a crimson. Suddenly he leaped from the ladder, grabbed the branch and raised it above his head. It shook in his fist as he shouted at me:

'Down on your knees, down on your knees. Master is vile, oh yes, but you, you—'

I went down on my knees. I put the question:

'Is it bad to love?'

He howled to the whole world:

'Man shall not love man! Man shall not love man!'

Then there was a silence, a calming down time, while he dropped the branch, then walked around the compound with his face in his hands. After a long time he motioned me to sit. He moved to a distance and then sat down himself. He spoke quietly.

'Friday,' he said. 'You are still only a savage and you understand little. But you have offered me a very bad gift. A poisonous gift. All I can say to you is . . . may God forgive you.'

He was right. I did not understand. But from that day I noticed that he was even more careful than ever that no part of our two bodies should touch.

CHAPTER TWELVE

In Which Coldness Grows Between Myself and Master.
He Schemes a Scheme and I Almost Commit a Serious
Accident

You ask me what happened to the baked pelican? We ate it
that day, but late in the evening, silently. It was not wasted,
but it should have been more enjoyable. The pelican is not so
important.

The days that followed Master saying man shall not love
man, were filled with work. Now here is a strange thing: before I lived on the island Master called Mine, I had never
thought much about work and certainly never worried about
it. Work, for us, is part of life. But the English word work
means – a kind of playing from which all the fun-juice has
been squeezed. Master believed very much in the value of
this dried-out fun, this work. He did not enjoy it himself, but
he did not believe that it was meant to be enjoyed. The English
God, apparently, had invented work as a curse upon the first
man because the first man had eaten a hard guava given to him
by the first woman. Yes, he cursed the same woman as well,
because she ate part of the guava which was given to her by
the snake, who was Satan the famous devil of England. Oh yes,
the Satan snake was cursed as well, well he cursed everyone he
could get at, that English God, in the early days, before his
son Jesus was born from Mary who did not copulate. When he
was born the English God did not curse quite so much, but
decided that revenge should be saved up for Hell.

Gradually I discovered that I was doing nearly all the fun-
less work, while Master would be engaged in what he called

Planning the Future of the Island or Thinking Ahead. Or he would be busy writing down what had been happening in his diary book, filling pages and pages even when nothing whatsoever had been happening. He began to prefer the company of that diary to me. Coldness was growing between us.

As I carried buckets of water from the stream or vegetables from the allotment, I would hail him with a cheery 'Fine morning again!', or 'How are you feeling, Master?' or 'Don't give up!' or 'All will be well!' or some such English greeting, but he would give me nothing in return except for a suspicious stare from his two blue eyes. Then he would lower his bushy-hatted head and return to recording something – perhaps the very manner of my greeting and his decision to answer it with silent looking.

More and more often he would engage in conversation with himself. Of course everyone must do this sometimes, but for Master such talk seemed to replace the need to speak with me. One night I remember I speared a boar in the moonlight. It staggered in the mud of a clearing, then I was in quickly with my knife to its throat. I was glad; the beast would furnish many meals. After trussing its feet with rope, I harnessed myself up and dragged the massive corpse slowly back to the spiked semi-circle of the stockade. The sky that night was a clean black-blue. The stars were arranged in the familiar pattern which spells out the old message to our tribe: Enjoy the Light. At least that is one of the many good things the star people are saying to us. Enjoy the light, I thought to myself, so I stood and enjoyed it, letting the light of the stars touch me. I glanced through a rifle-gap in the stockade, and saw that Master too was enjoying the light. Through his shining yellow telescope, he was examining the stars. As he stared at them, he was lecturing to himself and debating too. Because I wanted to understand what was happening in his English head, I listened carefully to all he said aloud.

'I don't know, I really don't know,' he was saying. 'If the stars are made of coal, they must be burning coal to create that much light. Yes, they must be white-hot coal. But surely you could see the smoke if they were that hot? Surely traces of that smoke would drift between the stars and the earth and hide or blur them? They're so sharp tonight. Sharp as glass thorns. Brighter than glass. What's as bright as those stars? Diamonds? They might be. Well, who's to say they're not? Gigantic diamonds. The stars might be gigantic diamonds. Rough diamonds, I should think. I don't suppose God would cut them into facets like a Dutch jeweller. No, I don't think he would. That would look much too artificial. God likes to make everything so that it appears natural. Yes. Well, if you found a star cut into facets everyone would think that it was man-made, wouldn't they, and God would get none of the credit for such a master-work.

'So the stars may well be giant uncut diamonds, great diamonds, spinning through space. Great diamonds like amazing, brilliant toy tops. Like vast marbles rolling around the universe. Good heavens, but if they're enormous diamonds, there's a fortune to be made up there. Suppose just one diamond star existed, not too far from the earth. A very small star, say about the size of London, well that would be small for a star. The thing would be to find a way of attracting that star down to earth. I could experiment with small, ordinary diamonds. Yes, I'm sure it would be possible to discover what attracts diamonds. And then the thing to do would be to construct an enormous diamond-magnet to bring that London-size star down to earth. But I mustn't bring it down in England – every Englishman worth his salt would take a hammer and chisel and break off enough diamond to keep him and his family for generations. There would be so many diamond pieces in circulation that they'd lose all value. Glass would cost more than diamonds. There's a real problem ...

'Where should the diamond magnets be sited? When I have invented the diamond magnets and patented them too, to prevent others from out-pacing me in the race for the diamond stars, I must place those magnets not in a civilized land, but in the midst of some great desert. The Sahara, that is the greatest desert I have heard about. And not too remote from England.

'Very well. I shall arrange my magnets in a great circle in the Sahara Desert. The diamond star the size of London will be drawn down to the sand by their power. Then, after giving thanks to God, I shall chip off a few pieces of star, place them in my luggage and ride my horse in the direction of Alexandria or some such Egyptian port. I shall sail for London, change my diamonds into a million pounds and begin to spend as no man in history has ever spent.

'Well, I suppose it is true that horses are not suitable for long journeys across sand. Very well, the journey to Alexandria will have to be made on a camel. So, before I begin the project proper, I will have to learn to ride one of those beasts. I'm sure it should not cost me much to hire a camel tutor in Egypt. Of course I must not tell him why I want to learn. Since I can ride a horse, a camel should not prove impossible. Perhaps, though, I should take two camels. For if my first camel should fail, through fatigue, disease or old age – and heaven knows I am no judge of a camel's fitness – I do not want to find myself alone in the sandy wastes with a London-sized diamond and a four-legged, humpy skeleton. They call the camel the ship of the desert – well, I've been shipwrecked before.

'Very well then, I shall take a spare camel. No, two spares, hang the expense. Three female camels, I think, to avoid rivalry. Good. Now I begin to picture it more clearly – the slowly moving yellow sand-dunes, the shimmering distant green haven of a far oasis, a sudden cry! What's that? A tribe of Bedouins galloping towards me uttering blood-curdling cries, hurling their spears and me and my three camels? It

71

could happen. It has been known. I could not survive such an attack on my own. Therefore I must engage some trusty companions. Not Egyptians, no. I would not be able to distinguish a trustworthy Egyptian from a villainous one. I must go forth on this adventure with Englishmen at my side. Now who is there in England I can trust?

'There's Paul the farrier, that's one for certain. He'd be good with camels and he's cheerful too. But wait a minute, didn't he cheat me playing cards at the fair? Aye, he's got a cheating streak, Paul will not do. My family? No. Though I miss them dearly, there's not one I'd trust with half a guinea, let alone a star. My old schoolmaster Fuller, he could be trusted with a man's wife, a mistress even. A saint, old Fuller, if he's still alive. But no, he's out. He would not last five miles in the Sahara, for trusty as he is, he's already dehydrated.

'Hm. There's only three that I can think of. Matthew Caper the baker. Jack Smiles the publican and wrestler at the Broiled Swan in Southwark. Yes, and the Reverend Daniel Hilton. Matthew, Jack and Daniel – all stout fellows. Matthew, Jack, Daniel and Robinson – sworn comrades in adventure ready to lay down their lives for each other, inseparable brothers, boon companions – that's the phrase I was looking for – boon companions. Yes, I trust you lads. Gather round and I'll tell you of my great discovery. Over the seas, in Africa, in the Sahara, I have entrapped a monstrous diamond. Ask no more, but come with me, and I shall make your fortunes. Come lads—

'A moment. Matthew in the Sahara? I think by now he may have grown too fat for any camel to bear him and too short of breath to relish desert life. Jack Smiles? Well, he'd be handy in a brawl with raiding tribes. But Jack might well challenge my leadership once we cleared the limits of civilization and travelled in lands where brute strength rules. And no doubt he could overcome me, with both hands tied behind his back. He his big teeth, has Smiles. The Reverend Hilton – he's a hard, thin man, trustworthy through and through. Neither is he a man of fear. A good friend to ride beside me through the perils lurking in that ocean of sand. A fine fellow in adversity.

'But what when we had won our goal? Riding home towards England, richer than all the kings of the world rolled into one, wishing to stop at every city and celebrate with feasting and most well-deserved enjoyments of all kinds – why, Hilton would be a most thin-lipped and disapproving comrade. Why, cheer up, Daniel, houris are traditional in these parts. When in Rome, do as the Romans – no, it would never do: Dan Hilton would damp all my celebrations.

'Why then, I'll trap that star alone. But here's another problem. Once I have taken samples from the star and am travelling back to England with those pieces to demonstrate the overwhelming nature of true wealth – who's to guard my star? I must conceal it somehow from marauding tribes and pirates. But how to conceal a diamond the size of London?

'Suppose I did take helpers with me. Stupid, native helpers. Hundreds of such unskilled workmen. Driven on by the whips of foremen. Then perhaps a great building of stone could be erected over my star to hide it from the greedy eyes of the world. Stone by stone rising over it until the great shining diamond surface was all covered, even from the gaze of the sun at noon. A pyramid! A pyramid in which to entomb my star! Yes, that's the answer. And after it is built, the men who built the pyramid will have to die, of course. And those who drove them on with whips must die also. To prevent them talking, to prevent them looting, to prevent a mutiny against my absolute power.

'Perhaps, that's what the ancient pyramids were built for. Perhaps inside each one, there's a great diamond. Perhaps. I must explore the pyramids. Yes. That would save all the time and expense which it would take to make diamond magnets and attract a star to earth. And then, if I find no diamond stars inside the pyramids, I can return to my first scheme. Well, we'll see.'

As well as talking with himself all this time, he had also been drinking with himself and walking up and down with himself. Meanwhile I was stuck with the problem of moving a heavy dead boar from outside the stockade to the inside. So I called out to him.

'Hey, Master. I've got an extra fine pig.'

'You've taken your time over catching it,' he shouted. Then he returned to studying the stars. 'I suppose that one up there could be Orion, but I'm not sure if it should be possible to see Orion from here.'

'Master, can you come and help me? I want to bring this pig in. But he's heavy as a rock. Take both of us to bring him over.'

'I'm studying the stars,' he yelled. 'You're breaking my concentration, Friday. Don't bother me with prosaic things like pigs when I am attempting to understand the infinite secrets of the universe. Get the pig over here yourself, use your brains, man, use your brains.'

I was angry. I pulled the swing ladder down outside the stockade. With all my strength I rolled that giant boar on to the bottom rung. I reached up for the rope. With both hands and the weight of my whole body, I gave a full-hearted tug to the rope. Up flew the ladder. The boar was catapulted up into the sky, over the sharpened top of the stockade and thud, down on to the earth of the compound, a hand's-width away from Master's feet. I know it was only that far, because, even after I had swung the ladder back, climbed up and over and down the other side, Master was still standing next to the hog, his body tight with fear.

'Friday,' he said at last. 'Look where that damned hog of yours landed.'

'It missed you, Master.'

'God's teeth! It was a near miss, Friday! You might have killed me! Do you realise that?'

It was true. I had been wrong in thinking only of my anger. I should have thought about Master as well. His death would have been an accident, but it would have been a great waste, especially after all my efforts to help him. In some ways he was quite insane, oh yes, but he had possibilities.

Master looked at me for some time with his head on one side. This meant that he did not believe in accidents. He thought, perhaps, that I had tried to kill him.

I said: 'I am sometimes stupid. But I have never been stupid enough to kill a man.'

He spoke very quietly.

'Lie down. Lie down and go to sleep.'

CHAPTER THIRTEEN

In Which I Make a Suggestion

Chopping down any tree should be an occasion. But when Master set me cutting down one of the highest trees on the island, the fun of the event was squashed out. First of all, he would not tell me why he wanted the tree killed. In that case, I said, I will not touch it. He asserted that he had good reasons for wanting the tree down, but that it was not my place to question his good faith. I said I was not worried about his faith, but I wanted to know what would happen to the tree. Because, of course, you are meant to tell a tree why you are cutting it down before you start. When your conversation with the tree has taken its course, and you have listened a great deal more than you have talked, and all seems right, then you may begin.

But Master gave a sigh and produced his watch and said I had six hours in which to fell the tree. I said that was wrong. I said that the tree would be wronged by such an attack. I said that I would be wronged by chopping at such a pace, that I could not enjoy such hurried effort.

So Master sighed again and laid a pistol on his lap. I was not ready to die. I laid my cheek against the trunk of the tree and spoke very quickly to it, in my own language. I told the tree through my tears, that it should prepare for the axe, that I was sorry, that I would make sure that its wood was used for a good purpose and that there would be no waste. Then I stood back, bowed my head to the tree, took up the axe and began the work.

Master fetched himself a little chair and his Bible. All day, as my axe sliced and cracked the yellow tree-flesh, Master read to me from his black book. He would read a few sentences in a hard, strong voice. Then he would turn over many pages, backwards and forwards, until he found something else he wanted to read.

It was early evening. Master read:

' "They shall be hewers of wood and drawers of water" . . . Yes, they shall, Friday, yes they shall.'

The great tree began to scream and lean. Master jumped up, clutching his book and chair to him. But the tree, of course, was falling away from him. He smiled.

'That will do for today, Friday.'

'But what's it for, Master?'

'For wood, of course. Thousands of uses for wood. Planks, boxes, brooms. Thousands of uses. Come along.'

I followed him back towards the stockade. We walked along the beach of small shells. I soothed my feet in the water as we walked. Along this beach were scattered the remains of many different boats which Master had attempted to build during his years alone. There was one which looked like a pig hut, another like Noah's Ark in the English Bible and another like a giant banana hollowed out and gone bad. They had taken many days of work-in-a-hurry, but none of them had managed to float. But as I looked at them, the idea came.

Master, whose mind was fixed on his evening drink and meal, was walking at an English pace. So I ran after him and tapped him on the shoulder. He stopped and turned on me.

'I told you never to touch me,' he said.

'I'm sorry, Master. But I have a thought.'

'Very well, Friday. Tell me your great thought.'

I knew he would not like what I said, but I had to say it.

'There is not enough love on this island.'

'Love?' he said. 'I've been here many more years than you have, Friday, and you don't find me moaning about the shortage of love. And shall I tell you why not? Because moaning does no bloody good at all, that's why not. Just what do you suggest? That we should pray for a boatload of women to be shipwrecked on the beach?'

'We must leave the island.'

'Leave the – oh, that's a fine idea, a very fine idea indeed. Why don't you bake a couple of loaves, pack our things and we'll start walking back to London now?'

'I thought London was across the sea.'

'When will you learn to understand sarcasm? Look, Friday, I've tried, during the years before you came here. I tried over and over again. I kept signal fires burning both day and night to attract passing ships. But no ships passed.'

I said: 'We should build a boat. We should use that great tree and build a boat. I think that would be the right thing.'

'But I'm no shipwright,' he said. He pointed back at his navy of beached, non-floating boats. They wore a sad look, like the skins of eaten fruit.

I said: 'But you have sailed on great English ships. I am sure you can make something better.'

'Perhaps, perhaps. But the journey from here to any British port would take us months, through storms and unknown currents.'

'But Friday's island,' I said, 'is only two days and nights away. I think I know the course to set.'

Still he held back. It was as if he had become contented with his living on this island, as if he was afraid of any other life.

'A ship,' he said, 'would take us all our time to build. And there's so much to be done. There's hunting for a start. There's fishing. Drainage has to be cleared and renewed. The stockade and the hut need constant repairs. There are clothes to be mended, goats to be milked, a look-out to be maintained. There's no time for building boats.'

'But I do all those tasks,' I said. Then I thought I should try to make him feel so good he would be eager to start work. 'And while I do them, you could build a very fine boat. You have spent so many years upon the sea – you understand the sea. And you have said yourself that the English ship is the greatest ship of them all.'

For the first time he seemed to be seriously interested, and he seemed warmer in his manner towards me.

'Well, I could do it,' he said. 'I'm perfectly capable of building a raft and sailing her as far as your island. But suppose I did? Your cannibal friends would eat me.'

I was so astonished at this idea that I could only shake my head again and again and say: 'No, no.'

'Oh yes, they would,' he said. 'That day when I rescued you from the savages. They were eating a man. They were from your island weren't they?'

'Yes, I knew them all well.'

'Well,' he said, lighting a pipe, 'that settles it. You don't catch me sailing to any cannibal island.'

'Master,' I said. 'When one of our people is killed, either by an accident or by warriors from another tribe, it is our way to honour his soul by eating him. So that a part of his soul lives on in each one of us.'

'You mean, you don't deliberately kill people so you can cook and eat them?'

'If enemies ever attack us, and there is no other way, we are allowed to kill them. But we could not honour them by eating them.'

'They wouldn't honour me by basting me over a slow fire and serving me up for supper with a tomato in my mouth?'

'What is a tomato? No, tell me another time, Master, it is not so important. Of course my tribe would not eat you. You would be treated as a guest.'

'Hmm. And perhaps I could teach them.'

I tried to imagine Master among my people. At that time it seemed funny to me, just funny. So I laughed and said:

'I think they would learn many things from you, Master. And you would like them. We have good music, good food, and good loving.'

Master tugged at his pipe, patting the smoke away from his eyes and staring towards the horizon.

'Two days and two nights' journey, is it? Perhaps, perhaps we could. Look, Friday, I'm making no promises, mind. But if I have any spare time in the next few years, I will make a seaworthy craft that shall carry us to your home. Perhaps.'

Gladness jumped up in me. I grabbed Master's foot and began to kiss it. But he pulled his foot away very quickly. He stared at me. Without him saying anything I could read the words across his brow: 'Man shall not love man.' He drew back his foot and kicked me in the ribs, once, so that I gave a very short cry. Then he turned and walked away.

CHAPTER FOURTEEN

*In Which I do Rights Instead of Responsibilities, Am Put
in Prison and Am Pursued by a Sad Hunter*

As the months passed and the memory of our friendship faded,
Master spent more and more of the time alone in his hut with
his busy thoughts. Sometimes he would read, loudly, from the
Bible. It was a book which often moved him to tears. Sometimes he would write for hours in that diary of his. And very
occasionally he would cover a few sheets of paper with designs
for boats. When he had drawn one design he would gaze at it
for a very long time before tearing it up. I worked hard at all
my various tasks, always hoping that one day Master would
emerge from his thinking hut, take a deep breath and begin to
hammer a ship together. But that hope became frailer and
frailer until the day the breeze blew it away. So that same
morning I rang the great ship's bell which hung outside his
hut. I enjoyed the noise it made, so I kept clanging it until he
shouted out:

'Friend or foe?'

'It's Friday, Master,' I said.

'Come in.'

I walked in and stood just inside the door. For to tell you
the truth, I was nervous of him. I did not like being in that hut
at any time. The musket was leaning there against his table.
Both of his pistols lay upon the table too. In order to stay as
calm as possible, I had brought with me a large carrot to chew.
I munched at it as Master continued to write. I munched and
leaned against one of the support poles of the hut, attempting
to seem relaxed. He wrote, I munched. There was a silence,

which I did not intend to break. For that morning I wanted to read his mood before he could read mine. And my mood that morning was stone. Eventually Master looked up and spoke to me in an even-toned but cold manner.

'You're back early, Friday. Working fast today, are you? Washed out all the pans? Milked the goats? Or were you hunting pigs today? I forget what I suggested last night. Oh, I remember, I asked you to take a look at the drains. How are they?'

I removed the carrot from my mouth.

'I don't know how the drains are.'

Master gave an unreal little laugh.

'But the drains are very important, Friday. If the drains go bad they might infect us both with terrible diseases. The drains are no joke. They must be seen to today. What have you been up to, then?'

'I've been swimming,' I said. 'My body agrees with the ocean. Today the waves are creamy but not too high. I have been swimming and diving off the rocks.'

I began to chew that carrot again. Soon I was going to have to tell him. He looked at me closely, putting down his pen to give me his full attention. He still spoke quietly, but now he spoke more tightly.

'But what about your duties, Friday? Your jobs? You know what I keep telling you. It's all very well to talk about your rights, all very well. But what about your responsibilities, eh?'

I threw the carrot out of the door and placed my hands on his table, partly to steady myself.

'I am not doing responsibilities today, Master. I am doing rights. And I think that it is now Master's turn to work.'

I could almost hear the explosion inside his head. But he was trained at his special school not to show emotion, so the only sign he gave was a convulsive blink.

'And what about the drains?' he asked. 'What will happen to them?'

'The drains say they will wait until Master takes up a spade and clears them. They do not care if they are clogged or not.'

'And what about our food? What about some fish? What are we going to eat tonight?'

'The fish have sent a message. They say they will come to supper if Master walks down to the fishing pool with a line and calls to them.'

'And the crops, Friday, the crops? Have you sown the barley yet, may I ask?'

'The ground says it is all ready to receive the seeds if Master cares to scatter them.'

'Any more messages? From the pigs, perhaps?'

'One more message.'

'From whom?'

'From Friday.'

'What's the message?'

'It's Master's turn to work!' I shouted.

Despite his time at school he could not contain it any longer. I jumped back as he started to his feet, grasping the edge of the table with both his red hands. I could hear the tone of his voice twisting higher and higher, tighter and tighter.

'You think I don't work? You accuse me of not working? How do you suppose we'd survive on this island if it wasn't for me? We'd be dead, wouldn't we? Dead!'

'I said: 'Friday fishes, Friday hunts. Friday lights the fires, Friday cooks, Friday mends the clothes, Friday digs the drains, Friday sows the seeds—'

The parrot shouted out: 'Goodnight! All will be well!'

Master tried to imitate a man who has suddenly decided to relax.

'Yes, and Friday does all those things very well indeed, doesn't he, Poll? Yes, you are a very naturally physical creature, you have a good hunting eye and supple muscles, so you work with your eyes and your body. But I am Master, and I work with my brain.'

'Has your brain built a raft yet?' I asked.

'I'm working it out,' he shouted.

Among the muddled heap of papers on the desk he managed to find a rough drawing of a raft, with many little marks around it. It looked just the same as all the other drawings of rafts he had showed me over the months.

'You see,' he said, 'I'm working it out on paper.'

'A raft of paper!'

'I'm working it out! Listen, Friday, listen to this. Who has the burden of making all the decisions on this island, eh? Who has to say when we shall eat and when we shall refrain from eating? Who is responsible for assigning tasks and maintaining morale? Who decides, with the help of God Almighty, what is wrong and what is right?'

The parrot was cheerful that day.

'Mine! Mine! God save the King!' it cried.

I ignored it.

'I would like to try to do that burden of decisions work, Master.'

'Impossible, Friday. That is Master's work. That is a very heavy burden indeed.'

'I am strong. Look how I lift the burden.'

I decided to demonstrate how it could be. I looked around and lifted up one of his favourite chairs, which I had made with a bamboo frame and pigskin seat and back. I set this chair deliberately opposite Master. I placed myself in the chair, facing Master across the table. I took one of his pieces of paper and stared at it. I played with a pen. I scratched my head. I made marks on the paper. I scratched my head some more. I crumpled up the paper and threw it aside. I opened the black Bible and muttered to myself. Then I looked up and said:

'What is for dinner tonight? Where are my shoes? How are the drains? Stand up. Go to sleep now. Light the fire. Go and catch a fish. Be quiet, Master, I am working everything out on paper.'

I lowered my head again and made more marks with the pen, drawing the pattern of a turtle's back. It was an odd but pleasant feeling to be Master.

He leaned across the table, snatching the pen out of my hand.

'That's enough, Friday. That's enough silly joking. What you have just showed me proves beyond any doubt just how absurd it would be for you to attempt any of Master's work. You don't know how ridiculous you look when you ape me.'

I cast my eyes down.

'Master, now I know what you truly think of me.'

'What do you mean by that?'

'You think I am an ape. You think I am a thing. I am just one of your possessions, one more thing that you can call yours. You can say – this table is mine, this lamp is mine, this hammock is mine, this Friday is mine.'

'Not at all, Friday. I never thought of you like that in my life.'

'I am a possession. Like that sunshade of yours. I am like those slaves you told me about. But when you told me about those slaves, you said you were against men who bought and sold slaves. You said you thought it was wrong to keep slaves at all. You said that, you said that.'

You must know I was not quite so angry as I was pretending to be. But in order to force him to think about me fairly, in order to keep him calm and yet force him into action, I had to appear to be angry.

'That's unkind and ungrateful, Friday. I have, all my life, been totally opposed to slavery and the slave trade. I am accounted a progressive and humane man among my people. And I have never thought of you as a slave. Never.'

85

'Then what am I? What am I?'

'You are an ignorant savage!' he shouted. Then he quietened himself. 'I am just trying to teach you, Friday. You are a man who works with me. Willingly. For the common good. Friday does Friday's work. Master does Master's work. This is called the division of labour and it is a very good system which has been invented and brought to perfection in England.'

'I understand about the common good. Those words are simple. Very well. I will work with you. I will share all kinds of work with Master.'

'No.'

It was time to tell him. I did not know what to expect. He might kill me straight away. He might scream and cry. He might himself die from the shock of it. But it had to be told.

I said: 'If I cannot share all the work with Master, then I will do no more work at all.'

That took a long time to reach the centre of his mind.

'You refuse to work?'

'I will do no work at all.'

Master picked up his musket. I had expected that. He pointed it at me and motioned me to my feet. Then he said:

'That is a wicked thing to say, Friday. Now you must tell me that you are sorry you said it. And you must beg me for forgiveness.'

'But I am not sorry at all. I will do no more work. That is all.'

'You will regret this decision,' he said. 'Out of the hut, come on.'

The end of the musket was cold against my back as he pushed me out of the hut and towards the ladder. I did not ask where he was making me walk. To the sea, to be drowned? To the place where my friends had been shot and laid down in holes in the sand? To a tree shaped like a cross where I might be nailed up and left to die like Jesus and all the others? As I walked I tried to stop thinking about the future. Master was forcing me to walk inland, down a thorny path we very seldom used. I protected my face from the sharp fingers of plants. We came into a clearing from which an inland cliff arose, a cliff of yellow rocks and pink-flowered creepers dangling. A place much favoured by small monkeys. There was a great crack in the cliff, like the mouth of a hungry giant. It gaped, dark and deep. Master pointed towards the stone mouth.

'You get in there,' he said. 'And stay in there.'

'In there? There may be wild beasts in there. There may be snakes in the darkness.'

'I wouldn't know,' he said. 'Never been in there myself. But in you go. You remember what I told you about bad men in England? They go to prison, don't they? Well, you have been very bad, Friday. And this is my prison. So in you go.'

'But what do I do in there?'

'You go in there and then you wait. You wait in the darkness. You think about the way you have wronged me in refusing the work which God has ordained for you on this island. You consider that wrongdoing until you have repented of your sin. And when you have repented, when you have decided to work again, Friday, then you may come out of the darkness. And you may come to me and say: Master, I am sorry. I will work. And I will say: Friday, you are forgiven, you may work, just as before. And I will forgive you then, Friday, for I am a reasonable man and not the kind to hold a grudge.'

'I am afraid of going in there, Master. But I am not going to say I will do all the work.'

'Get in!'

He jabbed at me with his musket. I climbed slowly into that mouth. I looked back once. Master was watching me. The floor of his prison cave was damp to my feet. On the walls around me grew small ferns. The roof forced me to bow my head. I cleared my mind of all thought of snakes, took a deep breath and began to feel my way around a bend in the rock tunnel. I heard Master calling out to me:

'It's for your own good!'

The breath of the tunnel was bad, as if creatures had died in there some time ago. By now there was no light ahead or before me. I had to stand still because I felt the muscles over my scalp tightening, also the muscles of my neck and shoulders. I talked soothingly to those muscles until they loosened. I concentrated my mind on taking pleasure in the surface of the cave, and this preoccupation chased away all traces of fear. As the last scrap of darkness fear and snake fear left my spirit, so I saw a scratch of light on the black ahead. A few steps and the light was the size of an egg. Calmly, calmly, I told myself, for this may be nothing but a vision or a crack too small for your hand. But my love for the light forced me to smile. The light grew bigger with each step. It was the size of my arm, the size of my leg, the size of my whole body, head included. I had found a back way out of Master's prison and I climbed out on to the sand of a little bay where we usually went only when crabs were required.

I had been in absolute darkness, the worst darkness I have ever known. But I had escaped to the light again. Across the ocean, the sun celebrated with its evening colours. Alone on the beach I danced, singing to myself:

> 'Thank you, light.
> Thank you, light.
> I will always enjoy you
> For that is all you ask.
> I'm enjoying the light.
> Let the whole world
> Enjoy the light.
> Let the sun and moon and stars
> Enjoy their own light too.'

When I had danced towards a good sweating and then blessed myself in the pink sunset waves, it was time for thinking again. I would not work for Master any more. So why should I return to the stockade? The island was big enough to hide me from him forever. I could live at one end of the island, he could live with his parrot and his musket for friends. I sat on the beach and began to plan my life alone. It would not be easy, but it could be done. As I schemed, it became dark and the moon rose. Suddenly I heard noises from the back mouth of the cave, the sounds of movement, sounds of small rocks crashing. Then, from the cave, came the voice of Master.

'This is no time for jokes, Friday. Hey, it's pork for dinner. Good pork. Look, Friday, you can come out now. Come out of the cave. Come on. We'll talk it over in the morning.'

I moved to the edge of the sand, under the trees' shadowing. I could see the flare of torchlight becoming brighter in the cave mouth, then the shape of Master, flaming branch in one hand and his musket in the other.

'Oh, come on, Friday, let's go home,' he shouted.

A nightbird called. Master jerked to a halt, pointed his musket. Then he realised that he could never hit that bird by moonlight, lowered his musket and began to trudge towards me. But I could tell he had not seen me. I let him pass me through the trees, then silently padded after him to see what he would do alone.

He searched for me, calling out every now and then. He walked to our patch of cultivated land, seeking me between the rows of vegetables. He went up to the little hut at the end of the vegetables, the hut I had woven for him and in which he kept his spade and fork, and flung open the door.

I watched from the undergrowth as he sought me among the goats. They nuzzled him, but he pushed them aside.

At the pool he stood alone and stared into the water. He called my name, or rather, the name that he had given me. I could tell that fear was entering his voice. He was afraid that I had killed myself, or snakes had killed me. Or that I had left him forever to hide in some remote part of the island, he might have guessed that. He stood very still for a time, then he began to shout. He shouted very loudly, and very slowly.

'Now, Friday, wherever you are, listen carefully. It is dangerous to be alone on this island at night. Dangerous. Friday. If you are thinking you can set up house on your own, think again. You can't survive on this island alone.'

He waited. I said nothing. Then he seemed to panic and started running off down a pathway. Towards me. I ran. I ran from him as fast as I could, branches brushing against my face. Behind me I could hear his noisy running.

'Friday!' he called, 'Friday! I forgive you!'

I ran on, faster and faster. Finally I came to one of the biggest trees in the forest. I climbed quickly on to one of the fat lower branches. I was about to climb higher, when Master appeared on the path leading to the tree. So I turned to a stone upon the branch.

Master was walking heavily, thumping the pathway with the butt of his musket. He did not see me. But as he reached the great trunk of the tree, terror gripped his heart. He stopped and shouted again:

'Friday! Don't leave me. You can't live alone. No one can live alone. Solitude tears you to pieces. It chews up your heart. It rips your brain with its claws.'

He was howling. He was in pain.

'Solitude! I've been there, Friday. It's a place of terror – like a great black cave. And you crouch there, you crouch there and you feel your mind turning rotten like meat. And you howl to God for the light of a human face – a face to look at. And I'm human – oh, come back – I'm only a man.'

He was in tears. And so was I as I stood upon my branch. I said: 'I'm here, Master.'

He said: 'Come down. Please come down.'

I climbed down to the earth, helped by Master's hand. We faced each other. We looked at each other's tears. Master nodded and smiled as he cried.

CHAPTER FIFTEEN

In Which I Become a Free Man and Strike a Bargain

That night Master suggested we both had a drink before re-
tiring. Good. I mixed into the bowl not only the usual in-
gredients but also the juice from the root of the vathi plant. I
did this so that we might sleep deeply, be troubled by no
jagged dreams and awaken with no clouds in our heads. So
morning approached us gently. I stretched in the early sun-
light. I performed a slow, easy dance to the sun in return for
its warmth. I strolled down the hill, enjoyed a good, easy-going
shit and then tried some high dives into the pool. Feeling simple
and alive in all my parts, I ran back to the stockade. Master
heard the ladder's creaking swing over the spikes and called
me into his hut.

He sat at his table. The musket and the pistols were on the
table, of course, but he was not touching them. Both of his
elbows rested on the table. His furry chin rested in his hands.
He was smiling at me.

'I have two things to say to you this morning, Friday. They
won't take very long.'

'Two things?'

Master stood up.

'The first thing is to congratulate you on coming to your
senses,' he said.

He stuck his hand out in front of him, its thumb on top,
palm flat and sideways. Odd. I looked at his hand, wondering
what this new signal meant.

'Take hold of my hand, Friday.'

This was indeed strange, for only recently he had taught me

most forcibly that I was not to touch him unless it was absolutely essential. But he obviously wanted me to take hold of the hand, and so I did.

'Now we shake hands up and down,' he said.

That was easy. We shook our hands up and down as if we were in that dance where only the hands and arms are allowed to move. Don't misunderstand. To shake hands in that way is not a love dance with the English as it is with us.

'We look at each other's eyes while we shake hands,' he said. 'That shows that we are sincere.'

My eyes looked at his. I was beginning to enjoy this shaking.

'Congratulations, Friday, on your change of heart. All right. Now we stop shaking.'

He let go of my hand and I took it away.

'What does it mean,' I asked, 'this shaking of hands? With us it is a dance.'

'No, it is much more serious than that when an Englishman shakes hands. It means that we are in friendship and agreement. It is done to prove that we do not have a sword in our right hand ready to stab at one another. It means we are at peace.'

'But might not a man carry a sword in his left hand and stab you while you are shaking with the right?'

'No Englishman would do that, Friday. Only a very treacherous person would sink to such depths.'

'An English Papist, maybe?'

'Some Papists might,' he said. 'But I advise you to avoid shaking hands with them in the first place. I'm sure I warned you about Papists before. Anyway, that's not what I wanted to talk about. I had two things to tell you. I've told you one, haven't I? What was the other? Yes. The second thing I wanted to say was this: I'm quite prepared to forget all about our misunderstanding yesterday. I will obliterate it totally from my mind. And now I suggest that you spend this morning washing my shirts and catching a few fish.'

I leaned back against the wall and relaxed the muscles of my body. I chose a thin, strong straw from the wall and began to pick my teeth with it. This time we would play the game right to the end. I would not soften or run away.

I said: 'I am not working. I am not working until all the work of the island is shared between us.'

He sat down, with one of those very deep sighs. He raised an eyebrow, tilted his head, then took up the musket and pointed it towards me. His face tried to remain calm. But I could see small muscles tightening under the skin around his mouth and nostrils. And I could smell that he was beginning to sweat.

'You are going to work,' he said. 'You are going to work as usual. Everything will be just as it has always been on this island. You will do your work.'

'The gun,' I said.

'Yes,' he said. 'The gun.'

'The gun is yours, Master. Yes, I know the gun.'

Little sentences. I was using rusty little sentences so that I could have time to think. I told my brain to move as fast as it could. It scuttled ahead, then it shouted back to me, telling me how to act. Obeying it, I put out my hand, grasped the barrel of the musket and pressed it to the side of my forehead.

'I have decided, Master. I will not live as a slave. You may kill me now.'

Master stood up, still holding his end of the musket. I could feel that he was trembling. His trembling travelled the length of the gun and bumped the end of it against my skin.

'If I kill you,' he said, 'I want you to know that I'm only doing it for your own good.'

This was an English proverb.

'Oh surely,' I said. 'You will not kill me in order to please yourself, I know that. For you have often told me, in the days of our first friendship, how it has saved your mind from rotting away to have another human being here with you on this island. And since, when you have killed me, you will be all alone on this island, all alone in the world, I know you are not killing me for pleasure.'

The parrot cried out: 'All will be well!'

Master said: 'Let go of the gun. Let go of it straight away.'

I kept my grip on it.

'When you kill me,' I said, 'I would like to be killed well. I think that if I hold the gun so that it points to this part of my head, where my spirit lives, then I will die very quickly. So please let me hold the gun. I am ready now, Master. Are you ready to kill me yet?'

That was all I had to say. My brain told me that it might work. I shut my eyes. How could I be sure my brain was right? You could never be sure of anything which depended on the mind of Master. For a long while he had no words. His breathing sounded very angry.

Then he said: 'I'm not going to kill you, Friday.'

Slowly I took my hand away from the gun and the barrel was lowered.

'I'm not working,' I said.

He gave a strange laugh and smiled, although smiling was very hard work for him at this moment. He made one last attempt to talk me round.

'Come on Friday, be reasonable. Work's got to be done somehow. Don't let's be silly.'

'I'm not working.'

Then he made an odd face and clicked his fingers in the air. These two signs taken together meant he had either been visited by an idea or by a message from his God.

'Shut your eyes,' he said.

'You're going to kill me after all.'

'No, I'm not. This is going to be a surprise. A good surprise for you, Friday. Come on, shut your eyes.'

The menace had disappeared from his throat. Instead there was a playful tone. I closed my eyes. I could hear him moving about. Then I heard the sounds of digging in the earth of the hut's floor. There were noises of wood and metal, then many small metal sounds. He sat down and told me to open my eyes. One of his fists was on the table, clasped around a kind of golden glowing, as if he had several miniature suns in his hand.

'Look, Friday,' he said. 'If you will do all the fishing and fire-lighting and other jobs, just as before, I will pay you wages. And then you cannot complain and call yourself a slave. For the difference between a slave and a free man is that a free man is paid – wages.'

'But what are these wages?'

Master opened his fist. It was full of metal discs the same colour as the sun at noonday. He let them fall upon the table with a chuckling sound.

'At the end of every week, when you have done all your work, Master will give you one of these for each day. They contain much magic. Look and see.'

He put one of them on the palm of my hand. I examined it very closely for magic signs. It had the picture of a man with a flat face upon it.

'It is pretty,' I said. 'It is cold. But what do you use it for? I can see it might be excellent for skimming on the water, even better than a flat stone.'

'No, it is much too precious to be skimmed,' said Master. 'That is a coin. A coin. You work for a week, I give you a coin for each day. You keep the coins. They are yours. At the end of the next week's work, I give you more coins. They are yours too. Soon you have many coins, all yours. And then, if you feel like coming to me and saying – Master I would like that copper kettle which hangs on the wall of your hut—'

'—You will say: No, the copper kettle is mine.'

'Ah no,' he said. 'For wages change all that. If you have coins I will say this to you: If you will give me ten of your coins, you may have that copper kettle.'

'But Master, I don't need a kettle.'

The parrot cried: 'Poor Robinson Crusoe.'

'Well, my lamp then,' said Master. 'The kettle was only an example. But this fine lamp, which I made myself, there's a lot of workmanship gone into that. That lamp would be, let's say, fourteen coins.'

'I see. So I can bring you coins. And you will give me kettles and lamps in exchange?'

'If you bring me enough coins, Friday, you will be able to buy anything at all from me.'

'Anything?' I asked. 'Tell me, for buying different things, I must give you different numbers of coins?'

'That's right,' said Master. 'Some things are much more valuable than others, you understand?'

I understand that.

'Don't worry, I'll help you with the coin-counting. I know that counting's not your strong suit.'

'I can count very well indeed,' I said. 'But I do not like to hurry when I am counting. I enjoy slow counting. You do English counting, which is very fast. But what is the hurry?'

'Never mind that,' said Master. 'I would like to introduce you to a new pleasure – shopping. This saw for instance, excellent saw, little bit rusty, soon brighten it up by rubbing with sand, this saw, might let you have it for eleven, eleven coins? How about that?'

He began to jump around the room, full of energy, picking up objects, naming their prices, extolling their virtues, setting them down and picking up other items.

'Bag of nails, here's a bag of nails, need nails to make almost anything you can think of, good bag of nails, all unused, two coins, two coins. Bag of sugar, fancy some sugar? Small bag for seven coins, sweet as sweetness. Knife and fork, very beautifully engraved with English flowers and the initials of an English gentleman on the blade of the knife — say twenty coins for the pair, twenty, only set like it on the island. White embroidered shirt, very rare indeed, beautiful craftsmanship and ideal for the evening. It's a shame to give it away like this but I'll let it go for twenty-two seeing it's you. Something cheaper, something cheaper? Very well — five coins'll get you not one, not two, but three home-made clay pots. Decorative and useful. Slightly wobbly, you say sire. Very well — four clay pots for five coins, that's a deal. And then of course you'll need a seaman's chest to keep all these things in. Seaman's chest, last you a lifetime, leave it to your children, heart of oak and it's all yours for forty, only forty little coins.'

He thumped his fist on top of the chest. It was a strange ritual. But I could not understand the reasoning behind it.

'But I use all these things anyway,' I said. 'I use them whenever I need them. Why is it that now I have to give you coins?'

Master smiled a very wide smile.

'Because you are a free man,' he said. 'You insisted on your freedom, so I give it to you willingly. But with freedom comes responsibility.'

I looked around the hut. Many of Master's things looked good. They shone pleasantly. But they would not shine any more brightly if they were mine.

'I don't really want any of these things,' I said.

He glared at me. It was as if I had insulted his property.

'Isn't there anything at all you want?' he asked. 'Look again. Surely there's something?'

I thought about everything he owned. I thought about work. I thought about wages. I conceived a slow but satisfying plan.

'Perhaps there is something,' I said. 'But for the moment I

will work and keep my coin wages. Tell me, how many coins would I have to pay you if I wanted you to give me your whole hut and everything that's in it?'

He stared at me, smiled, frowned, then smiled again in response to my smile. Then he laughed.

'You're a rascal, Friday,' he said.

'How much?' I asked again.

'It's a joke, isn't it?' he asked. 'It's a game?'

I smiled away until he had to smile back. I nodded. After all, it was a game.

'Oh yes, a joke and a game,' I said. I began to laugh. 'You see, if I bought everything you have, you'd have to work for me. And I'd have to give you coins so you could buy everything back again. And when you'd done that, I'd have to work for you again—'

Master was laughing too as he said: 'The hut and everything in it? I think I'd settle for two thousand coins.'

'Two thousand coins . . . that seems fair.'

Master put out his hand. I took it and shook it up and down as he had taught me earlier. After a while he told me to stop shaking.

CHAPTER SIXTEEN

In Which the Tribe Discusses Money

The tribe were laughing and crying, throwing their arms round each other in delight at the tallest tale that had ever been told on land or sea, drunk or sober. The oldest woman slapped 'Friday's' face gently many times and said:

'Your story's too absurd. I don't believe a single word of it. There is no such silliness anywhere on earth.'

He patted both sides of her face in return.

'You are ninety-nine years old and you still don't know that all true stories are absurd?'

However old she was, and the oldest person in the tribe was always described as ninety-nine, she was pleased with this answer. The doctor seemed more concerned, he was worrying in his usual fashion. It was said of him that he could see and identify the symptoms of illness even in a cloud.

'This Master was extremely ill,' he said. 'The fantasy of his that a man should work all day for the sake of a little shining disc of metal—'

'You have to imagine more than that,' said 'Friday'. 'First you have to imagine the big island of England. Then you have to imagine the many many many people of England all walking about hiding their bodies from each other with clothes, shaking each other's hands and singing God Save the King. Then you have to imagine them working very hard at digging coal and growing carrots and a kind of double size goat called cow. And then, once every seven days, you must imagine that they are all given shining discs.'

A relaxed man said: 'And they're happy with these discs? I mean they really enjoy that game?'

'Oh yes. For they take the discs and exchange them for food and drink and clothes to hide their bodies. And they give discs to the man whose huts they live in.'

'Are they so foolish they can't build huts of their own?' asked the doctor.

'I asked that same question. Master said that they could not build huts of their own because they did not own the land to build them on. The land belonged to the lords of the land. So the England tribe must pay discs for a place to live. This is called rent.'

The doctor said: 'His fantasy was extremely detailed, then? He had it all worked out.'

'Perhaps,' said the oldest woman, 'you thought it good to let Master play out his fantasies in real life? I mean the game of metal discs.'

'You understand,' said 'Friday'. 'I wanted to see where all his ideas of England would lead to. So I played every game he suggested. And I will tell you where that journey ended.'

CHAPTER SEVENTEEN

In Which I am Paid Wages

It was on my name-day of the week, Friday, and we were working together. The sun was huge and heavy on my back. I had felled a high tree with Master's biting axe machine. I had stripped its leaves, measured it, ripped off its bark and cut it down to form two good logs of the same size. Then I had to drag the logs across the heat of the sand towards Master.

Master was consulting a paper plan of his raft, and tying the logs together as I brought them to him. I was sweating like a river but I was happy, for the work was good work which I hoped would bring me quickly back to you, my people.

As I delivered the second log, dropping it into place beside the others, Master's watch gave chiming sound. This watch he used to tell him when it was time to get up or to work or to stop working. He would tell it at what time to ring its bell and it would obey him. He needed this watch because he was not accustomed to telling the time by the light, as we are.

This ringing meant it was time for lunch. So he stood up.

'Back to the stockade, Friday. Time for us to eat. And perhaps a good cool drink in the shade.'

You know how bad it is to stop work when it is going well, on a very hot day. Once you stop, you collapse and sleep fills you and the day has gone.

'Can't we have a quick fruit lunch here, Master. The raft is so important. Let's keep working.'

'You're forgetting something,' he said. 'Today is Friday. Today is your very first pay day. Come with me.'

So we walked back to the stockade. The shade of the path up

the hill was a relief, but it was hard to see after being in the brightness and I tripped once or twice over old, well-known roots. It was time for a good piss, so I began to walk away from the main path so that I could enjoy this secretly, as Master had taught me, but he called me back.

'But I am ready to piss.'

'That must wait, Friday. It's pay day. You must wait.'

'There is some pay day ceremony I must attend, Master?'

'Certainly. It is compulsory. It takes precedence over such matters as urination.'

Urination is a word I can say now, now that I have a firm grounding in Latin, but at that time I could not pronounce it, so Master allowed me to use the wicked word, piss. However, it seemed I must be paid before I could piss. And so I followed Master over the ladder, careful of my bladder, and into the hut, where he sat at his table. He took a little pigskin bag from a box. He opened the neck of the bag and smiled. I tried to lay spells on myself to stop myself from pissing, it was getting difficult to hold my water, I could feel its yellow bulge inside me. I jumped from foot to foot so that the aching would be fairly distributed between the left and right hand sides of my belly.

Master dripped coins into the palm of his right hand. They tumbled, slowly, golden, one by one.

'And so,' he said, 'here are your wages for your first week of work as a truly free man. One, two, three, four, five, six.'

Despite the pressure inside me I was counting with him, using my toes in order to be subtle. If I had used my fingers he would have seen my counting. Counting to six, that is easily done. But there are seven days in one English week. Despite my piss-ache I delayed pay day by pointing this out to Master.

'But the seventh day is Sunday, the sabbath,' he pointed out. 'You don't work on Sunday. I don't let you work on a Sunday. Remember the Sabbath day to keep it holy and stop shifting from foot to foot like that, Friday.'

It was true. He did not allow me to kill even the most tasty animals or birds on Sunday. No fishing. No jokes. I considered Master's Sunday laws until I realised that they were not absolute. I reminded him that he had never objected to the fact that I cooked on Sunday, breakfast, lunch and dinner. I recalled that he had instructed me that Sunday meals were to be of a higher quality than the food served upon ordinary days. I proposed that higher quality did entail more care and therefore more work.

'All right,' he said. 'So you cook on Sunday. But you can't be paid for Sunday … unless. I know, here you are, there's coin number seven. But it's only on one condition.'

'What's that?'

By now I was feeling like a big round fish because of the need to piss.

'I'll give you a coin for Sunday work on condition that you put it in the collection box after I preach the Sunday sermon. Yes, that's a good idea. I'm a fair man, Friday. I'll set the church money aside. None of it shall be used for my personal benefit or to further my particular interests. It will all be placed in the ecclesiastical building fund.'

'Will that be a good place, Master?'

'That will be very good, Friday. That money will mount up over the weeks and years. And when I have accumulated enough, I shall use it to pay you extra money.'

'That is kind, Master.'

'Extra money for extra work. I will pay you the extra money to build a chapel. And when the chapel is built we can worship there together.'

The parrot said: 'Praise the Lord. I love you.'

I said: 'Master, can I go now?'

'Well, take your money. What's the hurry?'

'I must have a piss.'

CHAPTER EIGHTEEN

In Which We Entertain Visitors

It was yet another fine day on the island Master called Mine, another fine and empty day. So I decided to fill it. One of the most delightful features of Master's hut, and it was, you understand, a place to be enjoyed, a place of invention and surprises, was a high-rising, pared down tree without roots. It was possible to climb to the top of this tree up a strong brown netting which Master had saved from his ship. At the top he had built a high but safe place from which all the coasts and inlets of the island could be observed. This was the look-out tree or crowsnest.

That particular day I remember well, for it was one of the few days on which I spent any of my hard-earned wages. I used one coin to pay Master if he would lend me his telescope for one day. Master's telescope was a wonderful creation. It was made of brass and brass is hard to describe. But it is a metal like a soft sun. Well, this soft sun coloured telescope, when you first saw it, it was just like a – I was going to say a straight and shining banana but that would not be right. When you saw it first, you noticed the shining more than anything. And then, at the touch of your fingers, it became five times longer than before. Stop laughing, it was a wonder, but I have not finished telling the wonders of the telescope yet.

At each end, the telescope has an eye. There is one giant eye and one dwarf eye. If you look through the dwarf eye, everyone looks like giants, if you look through the giant eye, everyone is small. It does not matter if you believe me or not, it is true.

So I had the telescope this day, and I was using it to the utmost, standing up at the top of the look-out tree or crowsnest. I remember sighting a monkey through the giant end.

'Hello, small monkey,' I called.

Just then Master started swinging his way up the netting and shouted out to me.

'Why's Polly all dripping wet?'

An anxious Master, worried about a wet parrot. So I explained to him.

'I baptised her, Master.'

He nearly fell off the net.

'Baptised her! But Friday, that's blasphemous. Animals don't have souls, you can't save animals.'

'I thought I would try, Master.'

'What the hell for?'

'I thought she would be company for Master in the English heaven, in case Friday never gets there.'

Master did not seem to have anything more to add to that debate. As he climbed up beside me, I turned the telescope around.

'Hello, large monkey,' I said.

But as I moved the eye of the telescope away from the monkey, away and towards the wide gleaming of the sea, I saw the shape of what at first seemed to be a huge insect struggling along the surface of the sea. I pointed, passed the telescope to Master. I guided it around.

'Almighty Father!' he said. 'That's a longboat. They're rowing ashore. But who are they? Where's their ship?'

He balanced the telescope slowly around. Then he saw it large at the same moment as I saw it, with my bare eye, small – an English ship, as big as many huts, floating upon the water, with Master's own flag flying above it.

He began to dance and shout: 'Friday! We're saved! They're English! They're English!'

106

He threw the telescope into the air with joy. It came near to killing me, but I dodged, and then collected it from the moss on which it fell. After all, I had paid for a whole day's hire of the telescope. I would make the most of it.

'Run back to the stockade, Friday,' he said. 'Run back and prepare a great feast. Food and drink, the very best we can muster. I'll go and greet our saviours and bring them back to eat.'

Master began to laugh as he ran down the hill. I ran back to the stockade and carried out orders, preparing the quickest and most exciting feast I could, plate after plate of attractively carved fruit, vegetables, fish and salted meat. From the revolting breakfast mush of our first meeting, I had weaned Master until he understood that a meal must be looked at first, smelled second and eaten third and that at each stage that meal must be accounted beautiful. While I was preparing the dinner, important things were happening.

Master told me later that his first impulse was to embrace the visitors. His second was to hide. He hid behind a bush. The longboat had by now been drawn up on the sand. Tall black rowing men were standing in the boat, passing empty barrels and baskets to the beach under the supervision of a lean white man.

On the beach, near Master's bush, strolled a large white man and a small white man. The large man was elegantly clothed, wore a wig and had a soft face. The small one was thin and wore a black coat. Both men wore pistols in their belts.

Said one, 'A highly picturesque spot, eh, McBain?'

McBain looked around him critically. He had been very well educated in Edinburgh.

'I'd say the Lord had been a wee bit over-indulgent with the vegetation,' he said.

Carey said: 'But that's all provisions for us. Plenty of water, plenty of fruit and – what the devil's that?'

What the devil it was was Master, who had suddenly over-come his terror, burst out of his bush, and was rampaging across the sand to reach them. McBain, naturally, reached for his pistol. Carey stopped him. Then, as Master tells it, he stood in front of them, almost drowned in his own emotion. The first white men he had seen in years, he told me, filled him with an overpowering urge to cry. Well, crying is good I said. No, he said, crying is not good, I did not cry. That is what he told me. I did not cry, he said, I clenched and unclenched my hands, which is an exercise I sometimes do to stop myself crying. And then, he said, then, I put out my hand and shook hands with them both.

'You are English?' said Master.

'Well he is,' said McBain, indicating Carey. This was, Master explained to me, a sort of Scottish joke. It seems that on the island of England there was not only the England tribe, but also the tribes of Scotland, Wales and Ireland. Now it seems – but that is a long, long story and not funny enough for me to waste the tribe's time with. I am telling the story of myself and Master.

Carey said: 'Introductions.'

Introductions is a custom which must take place before Englishmen may speak to each other.

Carey said: 'I am Captain William Carey of the *Enterprise*. And this is my first mate, Mr Amos McBain.'

Master said: 'I am Robinson Crusoe, English, a poor wretch cast away on these shores many years ago.'

The introduction ceremony was now complete.

Master said: 'You will take me off this island, sirs? You will, won't you?'

Carey smiled and then he said: 'Naturally, Mr Crusoe, naturally.'

It was then that Master began to cry but tried to hide each tear as it was born. And he made speeches through his tears as he led them back towards the stockade. He made speeches in which he thanked them, in which he promised them the pick of his vegetable patches, the pick of his goats, the pick of all possessions — not in exchange for anything but in simple gratitude. All that he told me later.

I was still working in the hut when the ladder swung over the stockade three times, and McBain, Carey and Master descended. They gazed at the dishes piled with patterns of yellow, gold, purple, orange, white, milky, brown, deep green, shallow green vegetables and creatures of the sea. They walked around the table on which these were set before they sat down.

Carey said: 'An impressive cuisine.'

Master said: 'Oh, that's the work of my man Friday. A savage when I found him. But I've taught him a good deal. Friday!'

I had put on my best clothes, but nobody noticed. I carried a tray with three most complicated and excellent blessing drinks upon it. There was much love in the way I had prepared that meal, much love in the way I had made those drinks. I put the tray down slowly and took three steps back, each step a blessing. All the time I carried the telescope under my arm, as a sign that I had hired the telescope for the whole day.

Carey said: 'Aha. Back to civilisation, eh, Mr McBain?'

McBain, seating himself and raising his drink to meet Carey's and Master's, said: 'How very handy for you, Mr Crusoe. Shipwrecked on a desert island and up pops your own personal slave.'

And suddenly I was full of poison anger. Suddenly I was weeping out of all my pores. Because Master had taught me there was one bad thing about his land. Slavery was bad. To sell slaves was bad. To be a slave was bad. To be called a slave was bad. Bad coming at me from all around. And I was no slave because I had said I would be no slave. So I said:

'I am no slave. I am a free man. Look.'

And then I took many gold coins, how many I do not know, from my pocket, and I held them up so they shone in what was left of the sunset, and then I threw them down on the table. Then I climbed over the ladder, out of the stockade.

Behind me, I heard their voices.

Carey said: 'A sensitive savage?'

McBain said: 'Powerful shoulders.'

Then I heard Master talking. Master said: 'Never mind about Friday. Let's drink to England.'

Carey said: 'England!'

I heard all three of them say: 'England!'

I did not go far. I did not want to lose a word they said. I climbed up behind the stockade, up behind the hut on to the patch of grass above Master's home, the patch of grass which overlooked not only the stockade, but a wide stretch of the ocean. And when I was there I put the telescope up to my eye.

First I looked at the beach where the longboat waited. The black men who had been rowing were carrying heavy barrels of water to the boat. They were moving in a line. Along the line moved a lean white man, who seemed to be throwing a long snake over them, but such a snake of such a length there never was. But when the snake jumped on their backs, they jerked as if they were bitten by some snake. Then I saw that their ankles were chained together, there were chains around their ankle bones, chains which are pieces of heavy metal in rings which ring inside each other and which can enclose and choke the limb or neck, chains which are too hard to describe but which are very bad. Oh, that was terrible, to see how those poor men moved.

Sweet tribe, I'll tell you more. I moved my telescope across the sea. And there I saw the huge boat which lay out in the bay. I saw the deck of the ship. I had heard of slaves from Master. But he had always told me stories of slaves escaping, slaves being converted, slaves being freed. But there I saw hot wood and tar and lying on it, bodies forced together, and more chains than you could imagine holding them, slaves, slaves, slaves, slaves. And much dying. There was much I could not see. There were naked men and women and children, with the chains on, and they walked round in a circle. I have told you nothing. But they were in a thousand hells.

So I had to tell Master. First I had to wait. I couldn't suddenly declare from the heavens that Carey and McBain must be wiped out. I had to lurk until I could tell Master what was happening. I listened.

Master had given them more drinks. He was toasting them and making some sort of speech.

'All these years,' he said. 'All these years I've dreamed of this kind of reunion, yes, oh yes. And I've tried to maintain standards here, I've tried to keep the old values flying and you know, well, it hasn't always been easy.'

Carey looked at his watch. I had by now crawled to a position exactly above Master's hut. Get back in the hut so I can speak to you, I was transmitting out of my silent head. But he was not receiving much that night.

Carey looked at his watch.

Carey said: 'Better be leaving soon or we'll miss the boat.'

Master jumped to his feet.

'Miss the boat!' he shouted. Then he slowed himself down, began to laugh. 'But – oh – I understand. A joke? Of course.'

Carey smiled. McBain smiled. Master laughed.

'Of course,' said Master. 'I'd almost forgotten about jokes. Can you wait a moment?'

Carey said: 'Of course.'

Master hurried into his hut.

'Just want to fetch a few of my things,' he shouted. 'Bible and parrot, you know. And of course there'll be presents for both of you.'

I was lying almost on the roof of his hut by now, so I could hear both his mutterings to himself and the slightly drunken conversation of the Englishman and Scotsman outside.

In the hut Master dug in the earth with his hands to reveal a box of gold.

The parrot cried: 'Poor Robinson Crusoe! Hallowed by thy name!'

Master said: 'Hallowed by thy – who taught you that?'

But I was not worrying about Master's religious difficulties. Out there in the compound, Carey and McBain were having a more significant conversation.

Carey: 'That Friday fellow should raise a good price at market.'

McBain: 'Aye – sturdy and spirited.'

Carey: 'Speaks English too. More than some do.'

By now they were engrossed together, so I lowered my head down through the ceiling of Master's hut. He was standing, his hands spilling full of gold, smiling. I appeared to him, telling him to hush, to speak quietly, and all he could say was:

'Friday? Have you been teaching Polly to say the Lord's Prayer?'

I said: 'They are bad men, Master. They are killing men. Their boat is full of people in chains.'

Oh, he knew what I meant, and you must love him a little for this, that he was very much against one kind of people putting another kind of people in chains, yes he was very opposed to such practice. Well, I opened his ears and he listened then.

McBain was saying: 'And what'll we do with this Crusoe creature?'

Carey said: 'We must auction him as best we can.'

McBain said: 'Auction him? He'll not fetch much.'

Carey said: 'Take him to Tangier.'

McBain said: 'Should he survive the trip.'

Carey said: 'Yes, should he survive the trip, we'll sell him in Tangier. He'll have a rarity value as a white property. And educated too.'

McBain said: 'Oh aye, he's educated. Even though he is half daft and totally decrepit.'

It was at this point that Master moved. He took up his musket and walked through the doorway of his hut. I knew what he was thinking and made myself ready.

McBain smiled at Master: 'Your man makes a good brew, Mr Crusoe,' he said.

Master raised his gun to Carey.

Master said: 'You'll not put us in chains. You'll not sell us.'

Carey said: 'Can't we talk this over like civilised—'

There was a great explosion and Carey was dead.

McBain was being clever, he was pulling out his two silver pistols, he was backing round to make sure that Master could not see him, he was getting ready to shoot Master down and so I dived, like diving into water and I closed the pistols round McBain's body and so, truly, McBain shot himself. Oh I held on to him because I did not know how many explosions might come from those guns, I hugged him and hugged him for so long, long after he could not stand on his own.

Then Master said: 'Put him down, Friday, he's finished. Let's take care of the rest of them.'

So Master led me in a charge along the beach. But the last of the visitors were rowing away and the shots of his guns could not reach them. They vanished, reaching the big ship which very soon became a small ship and then no ship at all.

'If only we could have captured that ship,' said Master.

I was more hopeful. Those men I had seen, I could understand their thoughts, yes even through a telescope.

'Surely they will find more men and come back and fight us?' I said. I was ready to make more preparations.

'I shouldn't think so,' said Master. 'They aren't warriors, Friday, they're businessmen.'

Oh it was late, late that night back in the stockade that the doubts came down on me like rain. I told my worries.

'Master,' I said, 'I thought you said that white men could not be killed by guns, because of science-magic?'

Master said, but only after some thought: 'Well, I laid that spell myself, Friday. So of course I can lift it when I like.'

I suppose I looked like a surprised goose.

'Come on,' said Master. 'We'd better bury them.'

CHAPTER NINETEEN

In Which Master Learns to Sing and Dance

It seemed to me that Master and I had come to terms. Therefore I decided to be more adventurous in trying to teach him. But I knew that I must do this without hurting his pride. One morning I saw him by the rocky river, sitting upon a log and reading his Bible book. To tell the truth, he should have been working on the raft, but he always told me that to read the Bible was the most important thing. I fetched one of the drums I had made and began to finger out a good beat, dancing along with it among the trees surrounding him. Then I began to make up a song for Master.

'The sun can cook an island
But the moon cannot even boil an egg.'

He looked up for a second, said: 'Hmm!' and went back to his reading.

'The shark spends his life praising the water
But the monkey is afraid to wet his feet.'

He raised his eyebrows at me, as if saying that my song was meaningless rubbish. He did not realise I was singing riddles to him. What a dull thing a song would be if you could understand all its meanings before it ended.

'The wind can tear a forest down
But the tallest tree cannot harm the wind.'

He continued to read as I danced closer to him. Last verse, I thought, last verse and I must make the riddle very clear.

'The body of Friday can show its happiness
But Master can only smile with half his mouth.'

Master slammed his Bible shut. Suddenly he understood.
Sudden understanding is the best kind.

'You're trying to make me lose my temper.'

I stopped dancing with my feet, just kept drumming a
little because I did not want to lose the music yet.

'I think you need to lose something,' I said, saying the words
in time with the drumming to make them easier to accept.

'Master,' he said. 'You must call me Master.'

'I think you need to lose something, Master. Why is it that
you never dance?'

I started to dance again to show him how good it felt.

'You want me to dance so you can laugh at me,' he said.

'Just dance, Master, dance! Good for the body, good for
the spirit!'

I did some big leaps – the pelican and the albatross – and he
began to smile.

'No, I couldn't dance. You would laugh at me.'

I thought about that.

'Well I might laugh, Master, if you make a funny dance. I
do laugh at funny dancing.'

'What about bad dancing?' he asked.

He seemed to know nothing at all.

'There is nothing funny about bad dancing,' I told him, as
if he were a child of six.

Master folded his arms, which meant that he was pretending
he would not dance, but could be persuaded if I tried in the
right way.

'No. I'm not going to dance,' he said.

'Come, it's so easy,' I said. 'Even the grass can dance. Dance
for me, Master.'

He shook his head. Then I had a good English idea.

'Dance for me,' I said, 'and I'll give you a coin.'

That made him laugh a lot. He balanced his Bible on the log, stood up, and girded his breeches.

'Right, Friday, it's a deal. Lend me your drum.'

'I should charge you a coin for borrowing it.'

'No come on, Friday, I only want to borrow it for a minute. You're the one who wants me to dance.'

'All right, Master. You can borrow it for nothing.'

We both laughed. It is very difficult to make a joke about money with Master, so I was very proud of that joke. I handed over the drum. Master began to thump on it, a strange walking rhythm which I could not grasp. He began humming to himself and then his feet moved to and fro on the ground. But his body and head were held stiffly, oh even his legs were stiff.

'No,' I said, 'you're not dancing yet.'

He kept moving, moving his feet.

'I'm dancing,' he said.

'That's not worth a coin,' I said. 'You're not dancing at all. Only your feet are dancing.'

'What am I supposed to dance with?' he said. 'My head?'

I was patient.

'Dance with your whole body. Dance with your whole spirit.'

He tried. He began to bump on the ground. It was something like dancing, very rigid dancing, but however difficult he made it seem, it still worked a little. I could see that the blood in his body was moving faster and making him more alive. And, for a change, he smiled with the whole of his mouth instead of only the right-hand side of it. He was sweating well. He threw the drum to me and danced on. He shut his eyes and circled round and round. Then he ended his dance with a huge somersault. He sat up and grinned at me.

I threw him a coin. He caught it, spun it up in the air,

caught it and put it in the pocket of his breeches. He was very pleased that he had danced, and so was I.

'You are starting to dance,' I said. 'But you must practise, you must practise until you dance as naturally as a two-year-old child.'

'How d'you mean, Friday? Little children don't know how to dance.'

'You watch when you next see one. Watch a two-year-old on a beach. He sees a crab. But he does not see it only with his eyes. His whole body aims itself at the crab. All small children show their feelings with their whole bodies. They are dancing all the time.'

'Well, that may be, but there aren't any children here for me to copy.'

'All right, observe the trees and how they grow. Copy them.'

'That's silly, Friday.'

'What is silly about trees?'

'Nothing. But people copying trees, that's silly.'

'I don't think you should copy trees then. I don't want you to do things you think are silly.'

'So you don't want me to copy trees now?'

'I want you to do two things. First thing is to stop thinking that to copy a tree is silly.'

'And the second thing?'

'Copy a tree.'

He thought to himself.

'Sorry, Friday, but it still seems silly.'

'All right, make me a song now, please Master.'

He waved his hands to and fro in the air.

'That I won't do. Not for love nor money,' he said. 'I don't make songs. In England songs are only made by riff-raff.'

'Riff-raff, riff-raff,' I said, enjoying the sound of it. 'Is that a song?'

'No,' he said. 'Riff-raff is a class of person.'

Master had told me that the tribe of England is divided into many classes. There is a King and his family who are the top class of all. Then there are lords who are wise about the world and bishops who are wise about God and talk with him. This is the second class. They are sometimes allowed to talk with the top class, but nobody else may.

Below them is a bigger class of men who give orders. These are called judges and generals and admirals. In this class you can also include some men who own a great deal of land or money. This third class is also wise, but not quite so wise as the second class.

The fourth class has doctors and teachers who are quite wise and the fifth has the keepers of shops who are not wise. The sixth are people who work with their hands, digging for coal, making pots and growing crops. There is also a seventh class which includes the very sick, those who will not work, the mad and the bad and most women.

'How low is riff-raff?' I asked. 'Are your song-makers in the third, fourth or the fifth class?'

'Oh the very lowest class,' he said.

'Riff-raff, I think I am riff-raff.'

'Well, who makes the songs on your island?'

'Everybody,' I said. 'We are all riff-raff, you see. Somebody needs a song, so he makes it.'

'Just like that?'

'Yes. Sometimes the tribe will go with boats on a shark hunt. Now a shark hunt is dangerous, but it's exciting. So the night before, we gather round the fire and somebody will make up a shark song.'

'What would that be?'

'Maybe I would decide to make a very strong, stamping song in which I boast about how easy it will be to kill the shark. He will roll over on his back and offer his throat to the knife. He will clench his teeth on a coral rock and get his jaws stuck. And so on. And I'd probably invent a chorus, so everybody could join in – poor old shark, you're as good as dead. That sort of song works well, everybody feels better, except the shark. And of course it works as a spell. Or I could make a different kind of shark song, a funny one. I would pretend to be terribly afraid of the shark. I would sing about how clumsy I always am in a canoe, how I'm always falling in the water, how I'm sure I'll get my toes bitten off, how I'm crying out to the shark – please don't bite me. That sort of song makes the rest of the tribe laugh and feel braver. So it works too, but in a different way.'

'And all your tribe make up songs?'

'Oh yes. Of course, some make better songs than others. But please, Master, sing one of the songs made by your riff-raff.'

'I've got a terrible voice,' he said.

'No, sometimes it is a good voice. It has many different colours in it.'

'But I don't sing. Except when I'm alone. Sometimes.'

I looked at him and knew that he needed to sing.

'But, Master, you are alone,' I said.

'Almost,' he said. 'Almost. All right, Friday, I will sing you a song. Won't sing it well. But I'll do my best. You do your drum thing.'

'A riff-raff song. Good,' I said.

The song was about a man and a woman who have some loving to do. So they go down walking among the corn. It is springtime, which in England is a time of new grass and small bright flowers jumping, cool sun and light rain. And the song said that the sky was full of birds singing while the lovers lay down together. I did not understand all the words, but the sound of the words was good. It was Master's favourite song and later on he taught me the words.

> 'It was a lover and his lass,
> With a hey, and a ho, and a hey nonino,
> That o'er the green corn-field did pass
> In spring-time, the only pretty ring-time,
> When birds do sing, hey ding a ding ding,
> Sweet lovers love the spring.
>
> Between the acres of the rye,
> With a hey, and a ho, and a hey nonino,
> These pretty country folk would lie,
> In spring-time, the only pretty ring-time,
> When birds do sing, hey ding a ding ding,
> Sweet lovers—'

Suddenly Master was on his feet and running away from me through the trees. I followed him, not knowing what wildness had suddenly torn into his mind. Beyond the trees he leaped along from one large rock to another till he came to where the river is deep and white. There he threw himself into the water. I dived in after him, threw my forearm round his neck, swam him back to the river's edge and dragged him on to the rocks.

'I liked your song, Master,' I said, to encourage him back to life. 'But if you want to kill yourself, that is not the best way.'

He was choking with water, but he managed to answer me.

'Not trying – to kill myself. Kill my desires. Cold water. Killing myself would be – a crime – before God.'

'And what will God say about the way you kill your desires?'

'He will rejoice.'

'He is a frightening God, your God.'

He sat up, stared at me with his great blue eyes, and then he shouted: 'He's meant to be a frightening God.'

CHAPTER TWENTY

In Which We Make Various Attempts to Leave the Island

Master had been mysterious for several days, whispering to the parrot and disappearing with various tools at odd times of the day. Of course I did not want to question him, it was obvious that he wanted to surprise me in some way, so I prepared myself to be surprised.

One afternoon he tapped me on the shoulder as I took four great steaming brown loaves out of our baking oven.

'Come with me, Friday,' he said. 'I've got a surprise for you.'

'Good,' I said, 'I am surprised already.'

I followed him down one of the lesser paths down to a deep creek. From the water into the trees he had laid many tree-trunks at a steep angle. At the top of this slide-way, wide, strong and topped with a flag, sat the boat Master had made.

I smiled upon it, for it had a confident look, the look of a boat which would sail across many oceans through seasons both rainy and dry. Its base was square, logs lashed together and over each other – a raft pattern I recognised from his paper plans. But on the raft he had built a hut, a hut big enough to protect both of us on a long voyage, a hut neatly thatched and timbered.

'Can we sail away, Master? To Friday's island? Can we sail today?'

'Hold hard, Friday. We'll have to stock her with provisions first, food and water. And pack my most important possessions too.'

'That won't take long, Master. Let's fetch them now.'

'Look, the boat isn't even finished yet. She's got a main-mast, but she needs sails before we can leave the island.'

I calmed myself down.

'Sails, yes. Well, we must wait, I suppose. But Master, does it float?'

'Well how am I supposed to – of course she floats.'

'Let me try, Master. To be sure.'

I persuaded him in the end. Together we stood behind the boat and pushed. It did not move. Even though the logs on which it was set sloped down so steeply to the water, the boat was hugely heavy and truly stuck. Master fetched two long branches, and we applied the leverage principle (which the English know as well as we do), but this only moved the boat a thumb's width towards the water. I took a big knife and scraped the bark off the slipway logs and that seemed better. But it was not till I greased all those logs with pig fat that the boat was willing to go.

'Hold it back,' shouted Master. 'We can't just let the boat launch herself. Hold on to her, Friday.'

I was left holding the boat, which was now tugging to go swimming. Master ran all the way back to the stockade. When he returned he was carrying a bottle of liquor. He waited till he had finished panting before he explained. My fingers were turning numb with the effort of holding back the boat.

'We have to christen the boat, Friday, just as you had to be christened.'

'Is that science or magic, Master?'

'It is tradition, Friday.'

He stood to attention.

'You'd better be ready to leap in, Friday. Soon as the bottle breaks you jump in the boat and I'll give you a push off.'

'What about drinking the drink?'

'Nobody drinks this drink. The drink is for the boat.'

'Good.'

'Ready, Friday? Right. I name this ship the Home and Dry. May God bless her and all who sail in her.'

Then he raised the bottle and struck it against the boat. The bottle did not break. He hit it again. Still the bottle was whole. Angry, he swung right round and brought the bottle down mightily on the deck of the raft. The bottle broke at the neck, his hand slipped and blood began to spurt from it as I jumped into the boat and went hurtling down into the water.

The boat hit the creekwater with a huge splash, reared up, then down, then bounced up a little. I began to sing as the boat settled in the water and began to move towards the sea.

> 'I am going to ride
> To the island of Friday.
> All the tribe will be waiting
> On the beach to meet me.
> There'll be singing and dancing,
> They'll be weeping and laughing.
> I am going to ride . . .'

But my singing stopped as the water rose up through the floor of the boat and over my feet and over my knees and the boat decided to lean over one way and sink as fast as possible. I fell backwards through the door of the deck-hut, and the deck-hut was not only falling sideways but filling very quickly with water, so that I had to swim clear through one of the windows, scraping the back of my head. By the time I reached the bank of the creek, the boat was almost all under water.

I shouted across the creek: 'It won't even carry me! It's no good.'

He shrugged his shoulders.

'Don't be so impatient, Friday. It'll take time, that's all.'

By now I had lost some of my faith in Master's ability to

build a good boat. But, watching the lovely flight of the pelicans, I had a different idea.

First we took long, strong bamboos and lashed them together to form a framework on the end of a black cliff. Then we extended this framework until it looked like a long bridge stretching over the sea but ending suddenly. This was so that we could run above the sea with wings attached to us and then launch ourselves from the end of the platform. (Below the platform were many rocks, so we could not have jumped straight off the cliff without certain death if our wings did not work.)

It became a game between us, who would make the first working wings. I was the first to try. I wore a pair of very long, narrow, graceful wings strapped to my arms and shoulders. They were made of the lightest branches I could find with material from old shirts stretched over them. I ran out along the platform, rejoicing in the wind and feeling it catch under my wings and out into the air, high above the – splash.

Master was next. He constructed some very large and smooth wings, that looked like parts of a machine. Along the platform he ran, but when he got into the air the wings whirled round and slapped him into the water.

I thought feathers might be the answer, so I constructed the wings of five hundred feathers. They were certainly the most beautiful wings either of us managed. But they carried me straight down into the sea.

Master tried with woven wings which flapped when he pulled little levers. He got wet. I tried with angel wings. I got wet. He tried with wings on both his hands and feet. Disaster.

We both still felt that flight should be possible. But we didn't know what was stopping us. We walked around all day watching birds, trying to pick up the vital clue. Then, one evening as Master drank his 'sundowner', a villain of an eagle flew over our heads, carrying a squealing baby pig in its claws.

'You cursed beast!' shouted Master, but by the time he'd fetched his musket the bird was gone.

But I had an idea.

'Master,' I said, 'why don't we try that?'

'What? You mean try flying with you carrying me? Or me carrying you?'

'No,' I said. 'No. It's an idea. You see we have been trying to fly by making our bodies part of the wings. We have been trying to be the eagle.'

'And we just get wet.'

'That's right. But why don't we try to be like the pig?'

'Like the pig?'

'Yes,' I said. 'What would happen if we hung below the wings?'

So it happened that we made a giant kite with a trapeze big enough for both of us below it. Every part of the framework was strong and most lovingly made. I painted the strong cloth which covered the frame with our own tribe's magic design, so that the flying machine would be drawn over the ocean towards our island and you, my own people.

By now we both had the feeling that the cliff-platform would bring us no luck. We carried our giant kite to a sloping, bare patch of hillside overlooking the sea. We stood together under the kite's green and brown expanse, both of us weighing our hopes and doubts as we stood side by side. Then, without saying a word, we began to run down the hill towards the edge of the cliff. We were jerked by the air, I lost my breath. Gradually we realised that we were flying, floating high on the wind. We still said nothing. We experimented, shifted our dangling legs from one side to the other to manoeuvre the kite. The currents of the air carried us higher. It was a pity that there were no clouds that day, for I have always wanted to enter a cloud. Now we were soaring in vast circles over the sea, gradually spiralling higher. I began to sing:

> 'We are going to fly
> To the island of Friday.
> Like the seagulls.'

He broke in, singing a line of his own:

> 'Like the eagles!'

Then we both sang together:

> 'We are going to fly
> To the island of Friday.
> Like the seagulls.
> Like the eagles. . . .'

I realise that it was not a good rhyme, but Master was a novice at making up songs. Besides which, it is not so easy to compose songs and fly at the same time. Gradually we stopped singing as we realised the goodness of flying. This goodness spreads through all your blood. Flying is good.

But at the very height of our flight, when we looked down, we could see Master's island and we could see the ocean. But Friday's island was much too far away. We both understood, silently, that while we could enjoy flying, it would not be possible to control the wind well enough to set a course. We began to circle downwards, finally crashing on to the sands and falling off our parrot-perch.

'Oh,' said Master. 'That was fun, Friday. Daft, but fun.'

We began to pick ourselves up. Master looked up at a flock of sea-birds cruising overhead.

'It is obviously the will of God that we should remain on this island,' he said. 'Tomorrow we will make a fresh start.'

'You mean we'll do some more flying tomorrow?'

'No, we will make a fresh start with our lives.'

'But every day we make a fresh start. Every day I am a new Friday and you're a new Master.'

'No,' he said. 'Don't pretend to be a philosopher. We must make ourselves better men. And when I say that, I am thinking particularly of you.'

CHAPTER TWENTY-ONE

In Which I am Given a Lesson in Education

Master spent several days in mystery preparations. He lugged a large piece of slate up the hill and over into the stockade, then tied it up on a special wooden frame. He sat on his drinking balcony in his rocking chair, sewing frenziedly at a piece of black cloth. Although his handiwork with a needle was untutored, it had a certain charm.

When I ventured to ask him what these activities signified, he put down his black sewing for a moment, looked at me and said:

'You'll see next Monday.'

So I had to wait, in some excitement. On Sunday I worked on the Chapel, for which Master had given me the most detailed instructions on paper. The main point about the chapel was that on the one hand it must be very carefully and lovingly constructed but on the other hand it must have only a white colour and no carvings because Master's God did not like any other gods in his hut. That was very strange, smoothing down each pole and woven square of the hut and then whitening it all until it all looked the same. It had a beauty, I could see after a time, but it was a very odd beauty – beauty with no eggs, beauty with no children.

On Monday morning, after I had done the early morning tasks, Master rang a bell as I climbed back into the stockade. Over his shoulders he wore a long black cloak. There was a long stick in his hand. I was pleased.

'Are you going to show me some English magic, today, Master? I should like to see some new magic.'

'It is not healthy for you to have such an interest in magic. Stop grinning and sit down.'

I sat on the ground and shifted my buttocks to make myself comfortable. Master walked up and down.

'That cloak of yours,' I said, 'it must mean you are going to dance. A black cloak? Is that for a dance to the night?'

'I am not going to dance. Just wait and I'll tell you what I'm going to do.'

'I will wait very happily, Master. Because I was able to wait for Monday, well now I can wait till a little later on Monday to know what you are going to do.'

'Be quiet, Friday!'

I could see his face was tight. So I stood up and moved towards the herb corner of the compound.

'You are angry, Master? Are your bowels unhappy? I dried those blue herbs. They'll make you happy again. I'll fetch them for you now. All I have to do is pour boiling water over them and leave them for a little. Then you drink the water. They've been drying just over here in—'

'Go back and sit down! My bowels are perfectly happy. Sit down and listen, Friday. I have been trying to teach you. I have been attempting to turn you into a civilised human being. And a good Christian as well.'

'I think you're doing very well, Master. I feel more civilised every day. The more we talk, the more civilised I feel.'

'And the more you talk,' said Master, 'the angrier I get.'

'Well, I don't try to make you angry. I try to help. But if you feel angry, please do not hide your anger. Let us share it together.'

'That's enough. Listen. Listen. When I started to teach you, I made allowances. Maybe I shouldn't have done that, maybe it's all my fault.'

'Don't blame yourself. Not for anything.'

'Don't patronise me! I'm not blaming myself. Listen. I decided that since I was teaching a savage rather than an English child, I should allow him to ask as many questions as he liked. To talk back at me as much as he liked, even to make fun of me now and then.'

'I laugh when I feel a joke,' I said. 'I don't know what else to do with a joke.'

'You feel too many jokes. You feel them at the wrong time. You laugh at things that aren't funny at all. But that, of course, is hardly your fault. A sense of humour is a rare gift. Quite common in England, but very rare among less sophisticated people.'

'You do not want me to laugh?'

'You may laugh when I make a joke.'

'That is what I do, Master.'

'No, you laugh often when I do not make a joke.'

'Perhaps you could tell me when you are going to make a joke, so I can be ready to laugh?'

'Don't be silly, Friday, that would take all the fun out of making jokes. Oh, God. Listen. I have decided to do something drastic about your ignorance. From now on, every day when you return from the morning hunt, there will be a teaching time.'

'Oh, good. I want to learn.'

'But teaching time will be different from our old teaching times. I will do the talking, because I am the teacher.'

'And if I—'

'And if you want to talk, you will raise your hand, Friday. And if I want you to talk, I will observe that your hand is raised and I will say: Yes, Friday, what did you want to say? And only then will you be permitted to talk.'

I raised my hand.

'No,' said Master, 'not now, I haven't even started.'

I kept my hand in the air.

'No, put your hand down.'

I put it down.

'You will put your hand up only when it is absolutely necessary. Only when there is something that you do not understand.'

Of course I wanted to ask about that, so I put my hand up.

'Put it down. The lesson has not yet begun.'

I put my hand down.

'Today,' he said and coughed in his important way, 'I am going to teach you about Education.'

He took a piece of small white stone and wrote on the great slate. He wrote big English letters. The letters shone, making a long shape.

'E-D-U-C-A-T-I-O-N. Education. From the Latin – Duco, I lead. I lead.'

I put my hand up again.

'Good question. What is Latin?'

Hand down.

'Latin is a language which was spoken by the Romans.'

Hand up.

'Yes. The Romans were people who many years ago lived in Italy.'

Hand down, then up again.

'Yes. Italy is a big country which is shaped like a boot. The Romans had a great deal of Education.'

Master pointed to the long word again. I put up my hand. Master spoke very slowly to me. He did not want to share his anger, that was certain.

'Yes, Friday, what did you want to say?'

I wanted to be sure I understood about these people.

'The Romans *used* to live in Italy, shaped like a boot?'

'Correct.'

'And where do the Romans live now?'

'The Romans are all dead now. That's not the point about the Romans. The Romans had a great deal of ED-U-CA-

TION. And they gave us this word. They left this word behind when they died. For us. I will now explain this word.'

I said: 'I am sorry about the Romans.'

Master shouted.

'You didn't raise your hand! Take care, Friday, take care. The first principle of Education is this. There is a teacher. That is me. Who leads. Duco. I lead. And there is a pupil. That's you. And you follow.'

I put my hand up.

'Yes, Friday?'

'What if the teacher loses his way?'

'Oh, the teacher knows the way. And if he does not always know the way off by heart, he has many books which will show him the way.'

'Are these magic books? Or are they books of fear like the Bible?'

'If you forget to put up your hand again, Friday, you will be punished.'

I put up my hand.

'What is punished?' I asked. 'Is it a principle of education?'

Master took a very deep breath, as if he was going to dive.

'Punished,' he said. 'Punished. It is not only a principle of education, it is a principle of life. It means to hurt someone because they have done something bad. It is not my invention. Friday. God punishes. If we live a bad life, then, when we are dead, God punishes us. But a teacher cannot wait until his pupil is dead. So a teacher punishes as soon as a pupil is bad.'

'But how does he punish?'

'Friday, you didn't put up your hand. Friday, that is very bad. You will now be punished.'

I was intrigued, so I smiled. He told me to stand up and I jumped to my feet.

'Hold out your hand,' he said.

I did so, but he did not want to shake hands. He turned my

hand so that its palm faced the sky, as if I was trying to catch rain. It was not raining. Master raised his stick, then hissed it down upon my hand with a burning hurt. Of course I closed my hand, pulled the stick away, broke it in two pieces and threw them on the ground.

'Friday,' said Master. 'That is very wrong. You must learn to take your punishment like a man.'

'I am a man,' I said. 'Look, if someone does a bad thing to someone else, they are punished. Is that right or wrong?'

'That is right,' said Master.

'Well, the stick did a bad thing to my hand. So my hand punished the stick.'

Master looked at me with a double-red face for a moment. I thought he was going to break me into two pieces.

'Pick up the stick,' he said.

I looked at him quickly, saw he was very serious, and picked up the pieces of the stick. I stared at that broken stick as Master had just been staring at me.

'You must learn to take your punishment like a stick,' I said.

CHAPTER TWENTY-TWO

In Which I Become the Teacher and Master Becomes the Pupil

Near the highest cliffs of that island, there is a stretch of short, tough grass. And out of that grows a twisted tree which seems to be in agony. It has great strength. It has few leaves. I felt a kind of brotherhood towards it. That was the place in which I chose to spend Sorrow Day.

I had been alone there for only a short time, squatting and watching and beginning to see, when Master approached me from behind, whistling and carrying a fishing-stick.

'Beautiful day again,' he said, stretching his arms and looking without understanding at the fast-running clouds.

'You know, Friday, I think God means us to stay on this island forever. Well, there must be worse places on earth. Anyway, I've decided to come fishing with you today. Just for fun.'

It is difficult to explain such things.

'I cannot fish today,' I said.

'Why not? It's warm and calm and the tides are right. And I'm in such a good mood today, it would be good to just relax and sit by the water.'

For Master, this was very good talking indeed. But he had not chosen the right time.

'The moon is wrong.'

'But it's daytime. There's no moon.'

'The moon does not die in the daytime. There is still a moon. And the moon is wrong. Can't you feel it?'

'No. I can't feel anything from the moon. Well, how about a

walk together? Shoot a few birds for dinner? I could just fancy a good casserole.'

'No shooting today. No killing of any kind today. No working today. No.'

'What's wrong with today?'

'You do not have a Sorrow Day in England?'

'Sorrow Day? Never heard of it.'

'There are certain times in the sky when the moon is wrong. And these are what we call the days of sorrow.'

'What are you supposed to do on Sorrow Day?'

'First, you must sit upon the ground.'

Master squatted down, smiling at me. He was feeling so good, he seemed ready to try anything. Good. I knew I must try and teach him about Sorrow Day. If he could learn this, then I might be able to teach him many ways of living, many ways of enjoying his body and mind.

'Good,' I said. 'Move your body until you are comfortable.'

'That's all right, I think. What now?'

'You must look at the ground. You must stare into the earth.'

He looked at the ground, but too busily, as if he was looking for a knife he had dropped.

'You must look into the ground calmly, without moving your head and eyes to and fro. Let your eyes stare down into the deepest part of the earth.'

He tried, but it was not long before he said:

'How long do I have to keep staring?'

'All day long.'

He laughed.

'And do nothing?'

'You must do a great deal,' I said. 'You must stare into the earth until you see the faces.'

'What faces?'

I was concentrating entirely on him now, trying to get him to the point of beginning. I could start again later. Come on,

Master, I was saying silently, you are almost there. Come on, Master, you are going to see a good vision soon and we will see if you can bear the weight of that vision on your heart.

'You will know the faces as soon as you see them. You must let your spirit seek them in the earth. And by and by, they will come to you. They always come.'

'Whose faces?'

'The faces of those you have lost.'

He was becoming more serious. He looked at the ground again, holding his head slightly sideways, suspiciously. After a very short time, he turned to me.

'I can't see any faces in the earth,' he said.

'You must be patient. You must be quiet. You will see the faces.'

He tried, but he could not hold his peace for long.

'Still can't see any faces.'

I did not respond. He should keep trying, his spirit was obviously unpractised in this seeking.

'Can you see faces?' he asked after another pause.

I nodded.

'Who can you see, Friday?'

'I can see the children playing,' I said.

'But you have no children.'

'My tribe has children.'

Master seemed to have forgotten about his own faces. He was looking at me in astonishment.

'Friday, are you the father of some of those children?'

'I may be. I may not be. It does not matter. They are the children of the tribe.'

He was losing his way, he was shocked by something he did not understand. His voice became louder.

'But Friday, that's terrible. You mean to tell me that you don't even know—'

'Quiet. I am watching the children.'

137

'But—'

'We do not talk on a Day of Sorrow. Stare into the earth. Have you lost nobody?'

Something happened, something good. He set aside his shock. He realised that he was setting aside some magic without discovering if it was good or bad. We both stared into the earth. We sat separately. We saw different faces in the earth. But at that moment we were closer than we had ever been on the island. Because I could feel the tug of the emotions inside that man, and I believe he could feel the emotions that were boiling sadly inside me as I watched the children. Suddenly he shut his eyes, and the tears began to squeeze out and down his crimson cheeks. I put my hand out and rested it on his shoulder to comfort him, then I resumed staring into the earth.

The doctor said: 'So he understood Sorrow Day?'
'Friday' said: 'Yes, he understood.'
Then 'Friday' stood up angrily.
He shouted: 'No, he understood nothing.'

CHAPTER TWENTY-THREE

In Which I am Given a Lesson About Civilisation

The day after Sorrow Day I awoke most happily. I thought I heard Master moving about in his hut, but when I called he did not answer. So I went to the sea, played in the waves for a time, then collected a bunch of bananas and carried them back to the stockade. As I climbed down the ladder I shouted:

'Master! It's time for school!'

There was a growl from inside the hut, a strange sound. I dropped the bananas and went to the door. At first I couldn't see Master. He was crouching in a corner, holding his musket. He was shaking all over. His eyes were red and staring. Cold anger flowed from him.

He said: 'You.'

'It's time for my lessons,' I said.

'You. You,' he said. 'Get outside!'

He stood up and pushed at me with the end of his musket. I moved backwards and out of the door. He grabbed at his gown. We moved into the compound. He gestured with the musket. I sat on my box.

Master moved over to the blackboard. He rested his musket against its frame. He wrote on the board the single word: 'CIVILISATION.' Then he turned to me.

'Today you are not going to talk,' he said. 'There will be no questions today. There will be no singing. There will be no dancing.'

I put up my hand.

'There will be no raising of hands.'

I lowered my hand and smiled.

'There will be no smiling. You understand?'

I stopped smiling and nodded three times. I did not understand anything except that a great wave of anger-poison was about to break.

'You don't understand!' he shouted. 'I will explain.'

He picked up his musket and began to walk in a large circle. I sat at the centre of the circle and told my body not to move.

'I think you are very dangerous,' Master said. 'I think, perhaps, you are an agent, a spy sent by the devil.'

I shook my head, but I did not look at him.

'Well, you wouldn't admit it if you were, would you? You wouldn't say, "Yes, Master, the Devil sent me to steal your soul," would you?'

He stopped walking.

'Don't answer me,' he said. 'Just listen to me. Later we will discover if you are truly the Devil's man or not. Listen. I have tried to teach you, most seriously I have tried to teach you. I have attempted to show you what is good and what is bad. But you take the good things I show you and you twist them and you tear them apart until they lie bleeding. You take the bad things I show you and you smile as if they were your closest friends.'

I tried to give no signals at all with my body or eyes. I could understand the fury of his words but I did not know what they meant.

'But yesterday, with your Sorrow Day, you showed yourself most clearly. Yesterday you nearly enchanted me. You were attempting to drag me into your own black, devilish religion. Yesterday. Yesterday, for a time, for a time, I lost my soul.'

It was time to try to speak with him. I tried to say my words as calmly as I could. He stood, amazed that I should speak.

'I gave you all I could. But you do not know how to accept a gift.'

'Your gifts were poisonous.'

'There is no poison in Sorrow Day. Sorrow Day is for everyone. It is a cleansing. It is a loving. It is still for you to use whenever you want it. You will never forget it.'

'Don't try to lay your cursed spells on me, Friday. Don't try to enchant me all over again.'

I looked at him and felt no fear at all.

'I think you are beginning to sing, Master. But I do not think it is a true song.'

He raised his musket and jabbed it at my back.

'Up on your feet,' he cried.

I stood up. He pushed me over towards the blackboard which said CIVILISATION. He turned me round with the gun so that my back was to the board. I could see that things were going to be bad. I decided I must wait and see what he would do. The possibility of joy on that island was dying, nearly dead. How much would it matter if he killed me?

'Stay there,' he said, and, still holding the gun, went into the hut. I stood very still, bracing my back against the blackboard. I heard metal sounds inside the hut. I began to compose and sing a song about Master. I danced as I sang without moving away from the board, without moving my feet from the ground, letting my body dance a slow, tense dance to go with the words.

'There was a man whose skin was covered with thorns
There was a man whose skin was covered with thorns
There was a man whose skin was covered with thorns.'

He came out of the hut then, gun on one arm and a great weight of chains and locks over the other. He began to chain me to the board. I offered him no resistance, except in my singing.

'May I take my knife and shave away your thorns?
May I take my knife and shave away your thorns?
So your skin may feel the fingers of the air?'

He pulled the chains tight around my legs and arms, he knotted and pulled the chains so that they bit my skin. I made up a verse in which I pretended to be Master answering Friday's offer to remove his thorns.

'No, no, I am disarmed if you take away my thorns.
I am disarmed if you take away my thorns.
No, no, for your knife hurts my thorns so badly.'

I was now chained and padlocked so I could not move. But I could still sing. Master suddenly tore off a lump from his black teaching gown.

'There was a man whose skin was covered with thorns
There was a man whose skin was covered with thorns
There was a man—'

He stuffed the piece of black gown into my mouth. I could sing no longer. I knew now that my death was ready for me. Master's spirit had become fevered, terribly fevered, so that his tongue began to speak nothing but fear and the mad language of fear. It was as if his part of his mind which refused to accept the lesson of Sorrow Day, was wrestling with another part, which understood and needed Sorrow Day and the other lessons I might have taught him. I have never seen a man shake so or hate himself so. He spoke both soft and loud, in starts and stops. He howled and whispered and all the time he held on to his gun.

'Today's lesson is about Man. Man. The earth belongs to Man. The animals belong to Man. So do the fish. And the birds. The trees. The grass. The stones. Man is the king of the earth. Under God.

'Does this sound good? It is not good. Man is not good. But vile. A vile king. A scarlet monster in love with darkness. Because darkness hides him. And it is necessary for a monster to hide himself. Hide himself away. Yes.

'But among those vile kings called men, there are some who can bear a little light. It hurts, but some of us can take the pain of that light. There are a few of us, only a few, to whom God has scattered a few grains of light. And we, my poor savage, are the leaders of men.

'Yes. I'm one of those leaders. A king of kings, a vile king of vile kings. Why? Because I accept my vileness. I accept my scarlet monstrosity. I accept it all. I bow down to those more kingly than myself, more monstrous than me. And I make myself responsible for those who are less kingly, less monstrous.

'I'm a vile king of vile kings because – because I use my will. Because what I take, I keep. Because I have a gun. Because I have a pipe, I have rum, I have a hammock, razors, a grindstone, an axe, three Bibles, ink and paper, two barrels of gunpowder, a pair of scissors, books of navigation, three Bibles, a hammock . . . mathematical instruments, crowbars, canvas, pistols, planks of wood, compasses. . . .

'Because I do not flaunt my body because I know it is scarlet and monstrous. Because I am ashamed. Because I am proud to be ashamed. Because money is the fruit. No. I don't mean money. Yes. Because money is the root. Because I am rooted in money and shame because I am the vile king of the vile earth because I came to save you from your monstrosity by showing you how dark you are and how monstrous. Because I am scarlet and monstrously white. Because I am – because I have a gun.'

He raised his musket to his shoulder. My eyes, which were raining tears, closed. Then the parrot cried out:

'I love you! I love you!'

There was an explosion. The parrot was a mess of blood and feathers on the ground. Master flung the gun away from him. He crouched for a long time on the earth of the compound, muttering to himself. He prayed on his knees, his shoulders hunched. In the end he stood up, walked over to me, took the cloth from my mouth and unlocked the chains which were binding me. He said nothing at all to me as he freed me, but from time to time he shook his head.

That was my last lesson. After that I gave up trying to teach him. I worked, he gave me coins, I worked, he gave me coins, month after month, year after year.

CHAPTER TWENTY-FOUR

In Which I Find a Use for My Money

The days crawled by like ancient tortoises. I worked whenever Master was watching. We only exchanged words when we had to – five sentences a day was more than usual. Only on Sundays, when I sat before him in the now-completed Chapel, would he speak for long. And then it seemed that he would never stop.

I kept a wary and sad eye on him. I noticed that gradually he was taking less and less exercise. In the first days after the chaining he would take long walks – the length of the island and back in one day – and would swim often. His walks became shorter, his swimming less frequent. After one year he seldom ventured beyond the stockade. After two years he very often spent days on end in his hut.

Most of the time he passed in studying his Bible. The more he read this book, the more he drank. He would sit at his table, his shoulders hunched over, his right fore-finger following the sentences in the Bible, his left hand clenched around his cup of palm-wine as he muttered to himself:

'So God created man in his own image, in the image of God created He him; male and female created he them. And God blessed them, and God said unto them, Be fruitful, and multiply, and replenish the earth, and subdue it; and have dominion over the fish of the sea, and over the fowl of the air, and over every living thing that moveth upon the earth . . .'

And then he would stare up at the roof of his hut as if wondering whether God would appear to him. I waited for my time to come.

My time came on a day when the wind was dancing. Master had gone for one of his rare walks.

When he returned, I stopped him outside the stockade with a gesture. Then I held in front of him a bulging sack.

'I have a surprise for you,' I said.

I tipped up the sack and out of it poured a great many coins to heap themselves on the earth in front of him. He stared, laughed and stared some more. I began to climb the ladder and over into the compound.

'Better count it all,' I said over my shoulder.

His voice was shaky and cold.

'You think I've got nothing better to do than count your money?'

I was in the compound now and almost at the door of the hut. I shouted: 'Not my money. Your money now.'

'I don't need money,' he shouted back at me. 'What use is money?'

By now I was in the hut and I did not answer him. I could hear him clinking the coins. A few minutes later I climbed up the ladder and looked over the top of the stockade. He was running his fingers through the gold.

'You're a rich man, Master. There are two thousand coins there. Count them.'

'What are they for?'

'You remember,' I said. 'We decided. The hut and everything in it. Two thousand. I shall sleep in the inner room. You may sleep by the fire. And guard me.'

He smiled and his eyes grew smaller.

'But there have to be two parties to a bargain. And I'm not selling.'

'Surely you remember our agreement?' I said. 'Two thousand. The hut and everything in it.'

He shook his head. He smiled.

'And look,' I said. 'Look what I found in the hut.'

I held up the musket. Then I climbed to the top of the ladder, stood on the platform, swung the ladder over and climbed down. As I reached the ground he walked towards me holding out his hand. I placed the butt of the musket against my shoulder. He took another step. I cocked the gun. He took four steps backwards.

'Now, Friday, don't do anything foolish. I've treated you like my brother. I've given you everything. When we first met, you were nothing but a savage. And I've educated you, as far as I could, despite your ignorance and your superstition.'

I looked at that sad man with his tangled mind and mangled spirit.

'When I first met you,' I said. 'You were a killer possessed by demons. Your head was full of nothing but your own power and your own guilt and the fear of a cruel God. And I taught you to dance, not very well, but I taught you that much at least. And I taught you to cry. But perhaps I was a very bad teacher. Because your head is still full of thoughts of power and guilt and fear.'

He looked at me holding the gun. He knew that the old lie about the gun not killing white men would not work. He knew that he had no lie which would weaken me.

'What are you going to do with me?' he asked.

I looked at him carefully. He was unfit now, but he would soon, with practise, become strong.

'I am going to make you work,' I said. 'You are going to work all day long. Instead of playing at work, you will work at building a raft, a good raft, with all your strength, all day and every day. And I will stand over you with this gun while you work. And when the raft is finished, we will sail to Friday's island.'

There was no argument. He started work that day. He wanted to start by drawing plans for a raft. But I pointed out that he had already made enough plans to form the basis for

147

a hundred rafts. I looked through papers and chose the most likely design. Then I handed him the big axe and escorted him down to a grove of straight trees near the sea.

The first tree took him a whole morning to fell. He hacked away at it, wasting most of his energy, and sweating greatly. For the job he used his usual goatskin shoes, breeches, waistcoat and hat. When the tree groaned and collapsed, he lay down upon the ground and hid his face. I looked at my watch. It was one o'clock. I walked over, tapped him on the shoulder with the musket. He looked up, exhausted and scared. I indicated, in the shade of a tree, a gourd of water, a piece of cold meat and some fruit on a tray. He crawled over to it, ate ravenously, then lay down and hid his face again. At half past one o'clock I roused him and prodded him to work.

But before he started to cut down the second tree, he did a strange thing. He removed his breeches, under which he wore long pants. He removed his waistcoat. He removed his hat. Without these clothes he looked very much smaller. He seemed thin. But as the days wore on the paleness of his back turned red, then crimson, then brown. His skinny arms grew real muscles.

And the raft grew. Each tree was sawn into logs. The logs were dragged to the water's edge. They were slotted together and lashed together. And one day the raft was finished. He pulled and I pushed it into the water. He stood on it, and it floated high in the water. He put his hands on his hips and, for the first time in months, he smiled. He was not smiling at me, but at his achievement.

The rest of that day he spent in loading the raft with water and food. When all our provisions were stacked on deck and the sun was sinking, we pushed the raft out from the sand and clambered on board. He sat at the tiller, I squatted on the deck with my musket. We spoke, because we had to speak, of the course we should steer. We followed the stars by night and he used his compass in the daytime. It took us two nights and two days. It was a peaceful journey. And now I am home. And the man called Master is waiting outside our meeting hut. And he has asked to be admitted to the tribe.

CHAPTER TWENTY-FIVE

In Which the Tribe Decides

Most of the tribe was upside down with laughter. It was good that such a story should have a ridiculous ending. That odd and hairy creature asking to join the tribe! They threw their arms about each other and guffawed. The doctor, worried, stood up and, by nudging them with his feet and making gestures with his hands, managed to quiet them enough for his words to be heard.

'No, no,' he said. 'He is serious. Yes. This Master wants to join the tribe. This is why the story is important to all of us.'

The oldest woman said: 'He would corrupt the tribe. He is too full of fear.'

The oldest man said: 'He might learn. And we might learn new things from him.'

'What new things?' asked the oldest woman.

'If I knew what they were, they would not be new things, would they?' said the oldest man.

The oldest woman threw some dust at him, but the oldest man persisted: 'He has never lived in a tribe like ours. He might learn. He has much to learn.'

The boy who had been taken out to be made better was sitting with one arm round the girl who had made him better.

'I think we should take him in,' he said.

The girl beside him rubbed his cheek with the back of her hand. 'He might betray us. He might put us all in chains,' she said. 'He might put us in a dark cave. He might make guns and kill us all.'

The boy shook his head: 'The tribe is stronger than him.

And I think the tribe should share its love with him.'

A very relaxed man who had been chewing a narcotic root all evening said: 'Oh, let him in. He sounds so funny. He would keep the tribe laughing—'

The doctor looked serious: 'He is a man. He is not a joke.'

The oldest woman said: 'He is not a joke. He killed three of our good men.'

'But he thought they were going to kill him,' said the boy who had been made better. 'And that was a long time ago.'

The oldest woman said: 'Have you forgotten them? I can remember them. Bentnose and Ivory and Weaver, he killed all three. Can't you see their faces any more?'

'It is a long time since I saw them in their bodies, but I can still see their faces. I see them every Sorrow Day,' said the boy.

'That is good,' said the oldest woman. 'They must not be forgotten.'

The doctor said: 'Let us speak to this Master. Will you bring him to us now? He may speak to us.'

'Friday' gestured to him to stand up and follow him into the meeting hut. As 'Master' entered there was a gasp from the children of the tribe, many of whom had not seen him, or had only had brief glimpses of him. They stared and giggled and whispered to each other. Their elders stared too, for the 'Master' who had only been with them for two days and nights had slept through nearly all that time, and he was still a great wonder.

'Master' stood at the centre of the hut, waiting, with his head bowed. The doctor raised his hand to still the children.

'Tell him that he may speak to us,' he said to 'Friday'.

'Master' began to speak, with 'Friday' translating for him.

'I don't know how to put this ... but I would very much like to stay. I know that I have wronged your tribe in the past, when I shot those men, but it was simply that I did not understand. And I know I've often treated Friday here more harshly than he deserved, but I was only trying to help him develop as a civilised human being. And, if you'd allow me to join you, well I do have a number of skills I could put at your disposal. And I could teach you many things about the world beyond the ocean. . . .'

'Friday' concluded the translation of that, in a voice of stone. Then he held up his hand to silence 'Master' and spoke to his own people in their own tongue.

'It is not for me to decide. It is for the whole tribe. But I will say this – that I pity him because he is sick beyond the reach of all our magic. And I think he would destroy our tribe like a great sickness.'

The doctor said: 'But if he has a sickness of the mind, we have many ways of curing such conditions.'

'No,' said 'Friday'. 'He does not have a sickness. He is sickness itself. He is a plague.'

There was a silence. 'Master' looked around him and saw the doubt on the faces. He beckoned to a small child. The child, a boy of three, walked up to him without fear. 'Master' put his arms round the child. He was obviously moved, the child was the first human being he had embraced in many years. He controlled his voice and spoke:

'Your children. Children like me. You see, he likes me. I could help you with your children. I could help teach your children. I could educate them so that one day—'

The child ran and 'Master' flinched back as 'Friday' stood facing him, a great spear in one hand and fury on his face. Two men from the tribe jumped and held back 'Friday'.

The doctor said: 'Drop the spear!'

The spear dropped. 'Friday' stared at the floor.

'Have you caught the plague yourself?' asked the doctor. 'Whatever he may have said, you must not kill him.'

'Friday' wiped his brow. Slowly he recovered his calm, and then he spoke.

'You are right. I am wrong. But he threatened our children.'

'No. Did he say he would kill our children?'

'I don't mean that. No. He said he wanted to teach our children. The children have no defence against his teaching. And he only teaches one thing – he teaches fear.'

'What are you saying, please?' asked 'Master'.

'I am saying,' said 'Friday' in English, 'that you must not teach the children because all you can teach them is fear.'

'Master' was at his most humble.

'Very well,' he said. 'I wanted to help. But if you like, I will not teach the children. I will even promise never to speak to the children.'

Now 'Friday' laughed, a hard and bitter laugh, a laugh that knew the ways of 'Master'. He turned back to the tribe.

'And now,' said 'Friday'. 'The plague makes promises. He promises that he will not even talk to our children. But who will guard him day and night? Who will stand on constant watch between the plague and our children? It is absurd for a man to talk of being in the tribe and not talking to the children. Without its children the tribe does not exist. I would say this to you. Remember the dead. And remember the children. Shall he join the tribe? Let the tribe decide.'

'Friday' stared at 'Master' as if he were a stranger. 'Master' lowered his head and waited.

CHAPTER TWENTY-SIX

In Which We Meet Again

The tribe decided that Master must return to the island he called Mine. We left him on its beach, with his musket and his Bible. He walked away, back towards the stockade and the hut which I had bought from him. He was welcome to them now. We sailed back to our island.

Many years later I was out fishing when high winds forced us to seek shelter on Mine. I was not sure what Master would do if he saw us – would he attack us. So I climbed, at nightfall, towards the stockade, stalking carefully so that I could observe him without being seen. I need not have been so careful. His bones were sitting in the rocking chair on the balcony overlooking the bay. The end of the rusted musket was at his head. The big toe of his right foot was locked into the trigger of the musket. So he had not been alone for long. I fetched the others. We dug a large grave for him. In the grave with him we placed all his possessions from the hut. Then we covered him with earth. I made a cross and placed it in the earth as is the custom with Christians.

I sang 'It was a lover and his lass' as a memory of what he was when he was most alive. My friends, seeing how downcast I felt, sang this song for me.

> 'The tribe changes
> As a tree changes . . .
>
> When the storm throws its weight against a tree
> The tree bends away.
> When the storm falls asleep upon the tree,
> The tree stands up again.

The tribe changes
As a tree changes . . .

The children are the blossoms of the tree,
They laugh along its branches.
The old are the fruit of the tree,
They fall when they are ready to fall.

The tribe changes
As a tree changes . . .

Nobody tells the tree how it should grow.
Nobody knows what shape it will take on.
The tree decides how it will hold its branches.
The tree decides when it is ready to die.'

On the next day the sea was calm. We sailed back home and
we told the tribe how the story of Master had ended.

DAYS OF HOPE

Jim Allen

From the Great War to the General Strike

In a Britain dazed by the holocaust of the First World War and the Russian Revolution, crippled by strikes and unemployment in the starving mining villages, men and women of ideals glimpsed the promise of freedom in the first Labour government, and saw it destroyed by political ambition and treachery.

Men like Ben Mathews, a starry-eyed volunteer in 1916, who deserts and ends up joining the miners in the big lock-out of 1921. Women like his down-to-earth sister Sarah, passionately in love with her husband Philip, but increasingly suspicious of his motives as he becomes one of the first Labour MPs and an ally of ruthless, domineering Ernie Bevin. This is their story, and the sweeping saga of the turbulent new era that shaped their lives.

Now a BBC drama series produced by Tony Garnett and directed by Ken Loach.

LIVINGSTONE

Tim Jeal

'A remarkably revealing new biography. Without detracting from Livingstone's incredible achievements, Mr Jeal describes too his faults and failings in such a way that the myth is destroyed but the man himself vividly revealed.'
Sunday Express

'. . . first rate.'
The New York Times

David Livingstone came from a Scottish slum and at the age of ten worked a gruelling twelve hours a day in a cotton mill. Thirty years later he had crossed the African continent from coast to coast and returned to England a national hero, hailed as the greatest explorer since the Elizabethans.

'Excellent . . .'
Sunday Times

'The story has never been more clearly and fairly told, and the judgements, both on Livingstone and on the consequences of his life work, look to be as sound as can be made in the light of the available knowledge . . . an admirably balanced major work of Victorian history.'
Washington Post

BEN HALL

Frank Clune

Australia in 1860. A time of exploration, gold rushes, gun fights and the cruel tyranny of the cat over transportees. A time when gangs of outlawed robbers and escaped convicts roamed the outback, bushrangers achieved immortalisation in song and legend. Men like Donahoo, Frank the Darkie and bold Ben Hall – men who'd rather die in a bloody battle with the traps than perish in irons.

This is the true story of those pioneer days, of the men and women who took the challenge of their new, wild, unmapped continent and tamed it.

'Ben Hall' is now a major television series from BBC/ABC, created and produced by Neil McCallum.